Algebra 1

Student Text

By Steven P. Demme

Miriam Homer

Math·U·See

1-888-854-MATH (6284)

www.MathUSee.com

Math·U·See

1-888-854-MATH (6284)
www.MathUSee.com

Algebra 1 Readiness Test

TO THE
PARENT Please read the "How to Use" in your instruction manual before teaching this course. Since algebra builds upon previously studied concepts, the first step is to have your student take the following readiness test. The answers are at the beginning of the solutions in the instruction manual. They may also be found at mathusee.com/downloads.html. If the test reveals gaps in the student's understanding, please contact your trained Math-U-See representative and find out how to rebuild your student's math foundation. This course assumes a thorough grasp of the four basic operations (addition, subtraction, multiplication, and division), along with a mastery of fractions, decimals, percents, and pre-algebra.

 Solve.

1. $\dfrac{1}{2}$ of 36 =   2. $\dfrac{2}{3}$ of 12 =   3. $\dfrac{7}{8}$ of 56 =

Fill in the missing numbers in the numerators or denominators to make equivalent fractions.

4. $\dfrac{2}{5} = \dfrac{\ }{\ } = \dfrac{\ }{\ } = \dfrac{\ }{20}$ 5. $\dfrac{3}{7} = \dfrac{\ }{\ } = \dfrac{\ }{\ } = \dfrac{12}{\ }$

Follow the signs. Reduce fractional answers, and rewrite any improper fractions as mixed numbers.

6. $\dfrac{1}{2} + \dfrac{3}{4} + \dfrac{5}{8} =$ 7. $\dfrac{4}{5} - \dfrac{2}{3} =$

8. $\dfrac{1}{5} \div \dfrac{1}{6} =$ 9. $4\dfrac{2}{3} \div \dfrac{7}{18} =$

10. $\dfrac{3}{5} \times 2\dfrac{1}{4} \times 4\dfrac{1}{3} =$

11. $4\dfrac{1}{2} - 3\dfrac{2}{3} =$

12. Change to an improper fraction: 6 5/7

Add or subtract the decimal numbers.

13. $\begin{array}{r} 8.63 \\ -1.85 \\ \hline \end{array}$

14. $\begin{array}{r} 7.0 \\ +6.38 \\ \hline \end{array}$

15. $\begin{array}{r} 21.052 \\ -.485 \\ \hline \end{array}$

Multiply the decimal numbers.

16. $\begin{array}{r} 4.29 \\ \times .5 \\ \hline \end{array}$

17. $\begin{array}{r} 2.7 \\ \times 3 \\ \hline \end{array}$

18. $\begin{array}{r} .005 \\ \times .08 \\ \hline \end{array}$

Divide and round to the nearest hundredth.

19. $5\overline{)16.6}$

20. $.04\overline{).033}$

21. $11\overline{)8.}$

Write each percent as a decimal.

22. 6% =

23. 45% =

Change each fraction to a decimal and then to a percent.

24. $\dfrac{6}{10}$ = _____ = _____ %

25. $\dfrac{1}{4}$ = _____ = _____ %

Follow the signs.

26. (–7) + (–24) =

27. (–6) x (–14) =

28. (10) – (–5) =

29. (–36) ÷ (9) =

Simplify.

30. -1^2 =

31. $-(5)^3$ =

32. $(-5)^2$ =

33. $\left(-\dfrac{2}{5}\right)^2$ =

Write in standard notation.

34. $2 \times 10^3 + 7 \times 10^2 + 1 \times 10^1 + 6 \times 10^0 + 8 \times \dfrac{1}{10^1}$ =

Simplify each expression.

35. $\sqrt{81}$ 36. $\sqrt{25}$ 37. $\sqrt{x^2}$

Answer the questions.

38.   What is the Greatest Common Factor (GCF) of 14 and 28?

39.   What is the Greatest Common Factor (GCF) of 56 and 64?

40.   What is the Least Common Multiple (LCM) of 5 and 8?

41.   What is the Least Common Multiple (LCM) of 6 and 9?

42.   What are the prime factors of 56?

43.   What are the prime factors of 75?

44.   What is the value of $|-7|$?

45.   What is the multiplicative inverse, or reciprocal, of 4?

QUICK REVIEW

Study these examples to review working with negative numbers.

When adding two negative numbers, the answer is negative. When adding numbers with different signs, find the difference and give the answer the sign of the larger number.

$$(-4) + (-5) = -9 \qquad (+4) + (-5) = -1 \qquad (-4) + (+5) = 1$$

Here are the rules for multiplying negative numbers:

A negative times a positive (or vice versa) yields a negative sign.
$(-3)(+4) = -12$ or $(+3)(-4) = -12$
A negative times a negative yields a positive sign.
$(-3)(-4) = 12$

Numbers with superscripts.

3^2 (three squared) is the same as 3 x 3, or 9.

3^3 (three cubed, or three to the third power) $= 3 \times 3 \times 3 = 27$

Be extra careful when squaring or cubing negative numbers. Notice how the parentheses affect the answer.

$(2)^2 = 2 \times 2 = 4$ $\qquad\qquad$ $(-2)^3 = (-2) \times (-2) \times (-2) = -8$

$-2^2 = -(2)(2) = -4$ $\qquad\qquad$ $(2)^3 = 2 \times 2 \times 2 = 8$

$(-2)^2 = (-2) \times (-2) = 4$ $\qquad\qquad$ $-2^3 = -(2)(2)(2) = -8$

Solve. The first two are done for you.

1. $(-3)^2 = (-3)(-3) = 9$ $\qquad\qquad$ 2. $-3^2 = -(3)(3) = -(9) = -9$

3. $(6)(-5) =$ $\qquad\qquad\qquad\qquad$ 4. $(-8)(-5) =$

True or False.

5. $8 + 6 = 6 + 8$

6. $5 \times 9 = 9 \times 5$

7. $8 - 4 = 4 - 8$

8. $36 \div 4 = 4 \div 36$

9. $(2 + 9) + 8 = 2 + (9 + 8)$

10. $(4 \times 5) \times 6 = 4 \times (5 \times 6)$

11. $(11 - 4) - 2 = 11 - (4 - 2)$

12. $(9 \div 3) \div 3 = 9 \div (3 \div 3)$

13. The commutative property is true for subtraction.

14. The associative property is true for addition.

15. The commutative and associative properties are both true for multiplication.

QUICK REVIEW

Study these examples of subtracting negative numbers.

$(-9) - (+5) = (-9) + (-5) = -14$ $(-9) - (-5) = (-9) + (+5) = -4$

$(9) - (+5) = (+9) + (-5) = 4$

Add or subtract.

1. $(-3) + (-10) =$ 2. $(-3) - (10) =$

3. $(6) - (-5) =$ 4. $(-8) - (-5) =$

Simplify by combining like terms.

EXAMPLE 1 $2A - 3B + 4A + 4B - 5A =$
$2A + 4A - 5A - 3B + 4B =$
$(2A + 4A - 5A) + (-3B + 4B) = A + B$

5. $5D - 6C + 8D - 3C + B =$ 6. $2A + B - A + 3B =$

7. $5Q + 3C - C + Q + 4Q - 5C =$ 8. $20 + 5X - 6Y + Y + 2X + X - 9 =$

9. $2X + 2 - X + 2X =$

10. $3Y - 1 + 2Y - 1 - 4Y =$

11. $5A - 6B - 3B + 10A - 8 =$

12. $18X - 5Y - 9X + Y =$

True or False.

13. Division is associative.

14. Multiplication is commutative.

15. Subtraction is associative.

Simplify by combining like terms.

1. $4Q + 2C - 2C - 2Q - 3C =$

2. $-5M - 7 + 3M - 4 + 5 =$

3. $2A - 3B + 4C - A + B + C =$

4. $4A - 5 - 2A + 7 - 1 =$

5. $4X - 3Y - 6Y + 10X - 5 =$

6. $15X - 4Y - 6X + Y =$

7. $15X + 6X - 4Y - 5Y - 14X + 10 =$

8. $3A - 4B + 6A + 7B + 8 =$

Solve. Use what you know about multiplying negative numbers to determine signs when dividing.

9. $(-3)(5) =$

10. $(-81) \div (-9) =$

11. $4 \div (-2) =$

12. $(-5)^2 =$

13. $4 + (-2) =$

14. $-4^2 =$

QUICK REVIEW

To multiply fractions, divide terms where possible, then multiply numerators and denominators.

EXAMPLE 1 $\frac{5}{_36} \times \frac{1\cancel{3}}{7} \times \frac{1\cancel{2}}{_1\cancel{3}} = \frac{5}{21}$

15. $\frac{1}{4} \times \frac{7}{11} \times \frac{4}{7} =$ 16. $\frac{1}{2} \times \frac{5}{6} \times \frac{11}{12} =$

To divide fractions, find the same, or common, denominator and divide the numerators. Change to improper fractions first if necessary.

EXAMPLE 2 $1\frac{5}{7} \div 1\frac{3}{4} = \frac{12}{7} \div \frac{7}{4} = \frac{48}{28} \div \frac{49}{28} = \frac{48}{49}$

17. $\frac{1}{3} \div \frac{4}{5} =$ 18. $7\frac{1}{2} \div 2\frac{4}{7} =$

To divide fractions using the short cut, multiply by the reciprocal.

EXAMPLE 3 $1\frac{5}{7} \div 1\frac{3}{4} = \frac{12}{7} \div \frac{7}{4} = \frac{12}{7} \times \frac{4}{7} = \frac{48}{49}$

19. $\frac{1}{3} \div \frac{4}{5} =$ 20. $7\frac{1}{2} \div 2\frac{4}{7} =$

Simplify by combining like terms.

1. $2A - 3B + 4A + 4B - 5A =$

2. $18X + 5X - 6Y - 8Y - 11X + 10Y =$

3. $4A - 4B + 16A + 7B + 18 =$

4. $-5X + 3 + 8X - 4 =$

5. $8K - 6 + 3K - 2K + 3 =$

6. $10C - 3C - 9D + 3D - C =$

7. $13A - 8Z - 2A - 12Z =$

8. $7D - 4D - 4 + 5D + 8 - 7D =$

Solve.

9. $(-3)^2 =$

10. $-3^3 =$

11. $(-6)(-2) =$

12. $(-4) - (-3) =$

13. $\dfrac{4}{5} \times \dfrac{1}{2} \times \dfrac{5}{8} =$

14. $\dfrac{1}{2} \times \dfrac{6}{7} \times \dfrac{2}{3} =$

Find the same denominator and divide the numerators.

15. $\dfrac{5}{8} \div \dfrac{1}{7} =$

To divide, multiply by the reciprocal.

16. $\dfrac{5}{8} \div \dfrac{1}{7} =$

QUICK REVIEW

In a multiplication problem, the numbers being multiplied are the factors and the answer is the product.

EXAMPLE 1   The number 12 has several possible sets of factors.
They are 1 x 12, 2 x 6, and 3x 4.
The factors of 12 are 1, 2, 3, 4, 6, and 12.

EXAMPLE 2   The number 5 has only one possible set of factors,
which is 1 x 5. The factors of 5 are 1 and 5.

Twelve is a composite number because it has more than two factors. Five is a prime number because it has only two factors, one and itself. (One is not considered prime because it has only one factor.)

Any composite number may be written as a product of its prime factors. A factor tree or repeated division may be used to find the prime factors of a given number.

EXAMPLE 3
$$18$$
$$2 \qquad 9$$
$$3 \quad 3$$
2 x 3 x 3

$$\begin{array}{r|r} & 3 \\ 3 & 9 \\ 2 & 18 \end{array}$$
2 x 3 x 3

Find the prime factors of the following numbers using either method.

17. 28

18. 42

19. 48

20. 100

Fill in the ovals with = (equals) or ≠ (is not equal to) and answer the questions.

1. $(1^2 + 2^2) + 3^2$ ◯ $1^2 + (2^2 + 3^2)$ 2. Is addition associative?

3. $[(81 ÷ 9) ÷ 3]$ ◯ $[81 ÷ (9 ÷ 3)]$ 4. Is division associative?

5. 3 x 4 x 3 ◯ 4 x 3 x 3   6   Is multiplication commutative?

7. 125 – 15 – 4 ◯ 15 – 4 – 125   8. Is subtraction commutative?

Solve.

9. $\dfrac{1}{4} \times \dfrac{3}{5} \times 1\dfrac{2}{3} =$

10. $1\dfrac{5}{6} \times \dfrac{3}{11} \times \dfrac{4}{7} =$

Find the same denominator and divide the numerators.

11. $1\dfrac{3}{4} ÷ \dfrac{7}{8} =$

To divide, multiply by the reciprocal.

12. $1\dfrac{3}{4} ÷ \dfrac{7}{8} =$

Find the prime factors of the following numbers using either method.

13. 16

14. 54

15. 72

16. 36

QUICK REVIEW

The greatest common factor (GCF) is useful for reducing fractions and simplifying other expressions.

EXAMPLE 1

Find the GCF of 12 and 18.

The factors of 12 are 1, 2, 3, 4, 6, 12

The factors of 18 are 1, 2, 3, 6, 9, 18

Underline all common factors.

The common factors of 12 and 18 are 1, 2, 3, and 6, but 6 is the *greatest* common factor, or GCF.

EXAMPLE 2

Reduce $\frac{12}{18}$ The GCF of 12 and 18 is 6. Divide numerator and denominator by 6 to get simplest possible form of the fraction. $\frac{12}{18} = \frac{2}{3}$

Use the GCF to reduce each fraction.

17. $\frac{24}{36} =$

18. $\frac{10}{25} =$

19. $\frac{30}{45} =$

20. $\frac{32}{56} =$

HONORS APPLICATION PAGES

The next page in this book is entitled Honors.

You will find a special challenge lesson after the last systematic review page for each lesson. These lessons are optional, but highly recommended for students who will be taking advanced math or science courses.

In the honors lessons, you will find a variety of problems that do the following:
- Review previously learned material in an unfamiliar context.
- Provide practical application of math skills relating to science or everyday life.
- Challenge the student with more complex word problems.
- Expand on concepts taught in the text.
- Familiarize students with problems that are present in standardized testing.
- Prepare for advanced science courses, such as physics.
- Stimulate logical-thinking skills with interesting or unusual math concepts.

HONORS 4-STEP APPROACH

Here are four steps to help the student receive the most benefit from these pages.

Step 1. Read
Step 2. Think
Step 3. Compare
Step 4. Draw

Step 1. Read

Most of the honors lessons teach new topics or expand on the concepts taught in the regular lessons. Read the explanations carefully. Sometimes you will be led step-by-step to a new concept. When doing word problems, think through what is being described in the problem before trying to work out the math.

Step 2. Think

It has been suggested that one of the major problems with math instruction in the United States is that students do not take enough time to think about a problem before giving up. One of the purposes of the honors pages is to train you in problem-solving skills. Start by deciding what you already know about the concept being studied, and then look for ways to apply what you know in order to solve the problem. Don't be afraid to leave a difficult problem and come back to it later for a fresh look. You will notice that these lessons do not have as many detailed examples as those in the instruction manual. In real life, individuals must often use what they know in new or unexpected ways in order to solve a problem.

Step 3. Compare

◈ Compare your solution to the one in the back of the instruction manual. If you solved the problem differently, see whether you can follow the given solution. There is often more than one way to solve a problem. The solutions may also give you hints that are not on the lesson pages. If you are not able to solve a problem on your own, do not be upset. Much of this material was purposely designed to stretch your math muscles. You will learn a great deal by giving a problem your best try and then studying the solution.

Step 4. Draw

◈ When in doubt, draw! Often a picture will help you see the big picture and recognize which math skills are necessary to solve the problem.

SCHEDULING HONORS PAGES

Students may not need to do all of the lesson practice pages for each lesson. We do recommend a student finish all of the systematic review pages before attempting the honors page.

If a student needs more time to become comfortable with the new concepts in the text before tackling more advanced problems, he may delay an honors page until he is two or three lessons ahead in the course. The student may also spread one honors section over two or three days while continuing to do the regular student pages. This approach allows time to come back to difficult problems for a fresh look.

Another option is to tackle all the honors pages after finishing the book as a review and as preparation for the next level. This approach works especially well if you are continuing your study through the summer months.

If you have a pre-2009 teacher manual, go online to mathusee.com/2009solutions.html to access the honors solutions.

If you have a pre-2009 teacher manual, go online to mathusee.com/2009solutions. html to access the honors solutions.

These problems are designed to help you practice thinking skills, fractions, and negative numbers.

1. Martha wants to make the cookie recipe shown below. She plans to make one and one-half times the amount shown. Write the new amount of each ingredient in the blanks. (Round the eggs to the nearest whole egg.)

    _____ 2/3 cup shortening   _____ 1 3/4 teaspoon
                                                          baking powder

    _____ 3/4 cup sugar   _____ 1/2 teaspoon salt

    _____ 1 egg   _____ 3/4 cup rolled oats

    _____ 1 tablespoon milk   _____ 1/4 cup dried fruit

    _____ 1 teaspoon vanilla

    Makes 3 dozen cookies

2. When Martha had all the ingredients in the bowl, it was too full to stir easily, so she divided the dough into two bowls. Assuming she has divided the dough evenly, how many cookies can she expect to get from each bowl of dough?

3. Daniel has $1,609.00 with which to pay his monthly bills. This month's bills are: electric company—$35.92, telephone company—$25.26, heating oil—$255.10, mortgage—$798.53, trash collection—$20, doctor—$116.48, car repairs—$398.19. After Daniel has paid all that he can, how much money will he actually have? Write your answer as a positive or negative number.

4. The water level in a pond dropped three inches a day during the hot weather. After dropping at that rate for six days, the water level increased five inches during a rain storm. Using positive and negative numbers, find the water level at the end of the storm, as compared to the level at the beginning of the hot weather.

5. Tanny was hired to do four days of work. Her boss gave her two options for payment. The first option is to start with $10 a day and double the previous day's pay for each of the four days. The second option is to start with $5 a day and square the previous day's pay for each of the four days. Which option should Tanny choose?

Here are some problems to help you think about the commutative and associative properties.

6. Alisha packed four Christmas gifts in each of three boxes. Shayla packed three gifts in each of four boxes. Compare the total number of gifts each girl packed. What property does this illustrate?

7. Kaylin put five apples and six oranges in one bag. She put eight pears in another bag. Jenna put five apples in one bag. She put six oranges and eight pears in another bag. Compare the total number of pieces of fruit each girl has. What property does this illustrate?

8. Eight pizzas were divided among four people. The next day, four pizzas were divided among eight people. Compare the amount of pizza each person received on the different days. What does this illustrate about the commutative property?

Suggestion: Try writing your own word problems to illustrate which operations are associative or commutative.

QUICK REVIEW

The least common multiple (LCM) is useful for finding the smallest possible common denominator of two fractions that are to be added or subtracted.

EXAMPLE 1 Multiples of 6 are 6, 12, 18, 24, 36, 42, 48, 54, 60, 66, 72 . . .
Multiples of 8 are 8, 16, 24, 32, 40, 48, 56, 64, 72, 80 . . .
Multiples that are common to both 6 and 8 are 24, 48, and 72, and the smallest, or *least*, common multiple is 24.

EXAMPLE 2 Add using LCM for the common denominator.

$\dfrac{3}{8} = \dfrac{9}{24}$ What times 8 is 24? The answer is 3, and 3 times 3 is 9.

$+\dfrac{1}{6} = \dfrac{4}{24}$ What times 6 is 24? The answer is 4, and 4 times 1 is 4.

$\dfrac{13}{24}$ If you use the LCM to add or subtract, your answer may not need to be reduced.

Find the LCM, and add or subtract. (Practice 2B reviews a shorter method for finding LCM. Use whichever method you wish.)

1. $\dfrac{3}{8}$
    $+\dfrac{1}{4}$

2. $\dfrac{5}{6}$
    $-\dfrac{3}{10}$

3. $\dfrac{2}{3}$
    $+\dfrac{4}{5}$

Use **PARA**chute **EX**pert **M**y **D**ear **A**unt **S**ally to simplify each expression.

4. $5 \cdot 6 + 4^2 =$

5. $9 \cdot 4^2 - 19 =$

6. $6^2 \cdot 8 \div 2 =$

7. $12 \cdot 3 + 4^2 - 8 =$

8. $18 \div 2 \cdot 5 + 6 =$

9. $(-3)^2 + (8 + 3^2) =$

10. $8 + 32 \div 4 - 2^2$

11. $3A - 3B + 5A + 4B + 7 =$

12. $|5 \cdot 6^2| =$

13. $|18 + 2^3| =$

14. $|3^2 - 8^2| =$

15. $|4^2 - 2^2| =$

QUICK REVIEW

Least common multiple (LCM) may be found without listing the multiples.

EXAMPLE 1 Find the LCM of 15 and 18. First list the prime factors of each number.

15 = 3 x 5
18 = 2 x 3 x 3

LCM = 2 x 3 x 3 x 5 = 90

The LCM must contain each of the factors in the original numbers. The 3 must be used twice because that is the most number of times it is used in one number.

You may check by division to see that 15 and 18 are both factors of 90.

EXAMPLE 2 Find the LCM of 12 and 25. First list the prime factors of each number. We use 2 and 5 twice as factors because they are used twice in the original numbers.

12 = 2 x 2 x 3
25 = 5 x 5
LCM = 2 x 2 x 3 x 5 x 5 = 300

You may check by division to see that 12 and 25 are both factors of 300.

Use the factoring method to find the LCM.

1. 16 and 18

2. 10 and 14

3. 24 and 50

Use **PARA**chute **EX**pert **M**y **D**ear **A**unt **S**ally to simplify each expression.

4. $4 \cdot 8 + 3^2 =$

5. $10 \cdot 4^2 - 25 =$

6. $7^2 - 9 \div 2 =$

7. $18 \cdot 2 + 5^2 - 11 =$

8. $15 \div 3 \cdot 8 + 10 =$

9. $(-5)^2 + (9 + 4^2) =$

10. $9^2 + 48 \div 12 - 3^3$

11. $|4^2 - 9| + (8 \div 4)^2 =$

12. $|3^2 - 5^2| - (15 \div 3)^3 + 18 =$

13. $|10^2 - 5^2| + |-8 + 2^2| =$

14. $|18 - 36| + (|3 - 5^2| - 15)^2 =$

15. $|(-10)^2 - 9| - |2^4 - 5^2| =$

Use the correct order of operations to simplify.

1. $4 \cdot 7 + 3^2 =$

2. $5^2 + 8 \div 2 =$

3. $12^2 \times (2 + 3) - 4 =$

4. $9 \times 1^2 - 8 =$

5. $14 \div 2 - 1 \times 6 =$

6. $6 + 28 \div 7 - 4^2 =$

7. $(-3)^2 \div 9 + 6 =$

8. $|6 \div (-2)| \times 5 + 3^2 =$

Solve.

9. $\dfrac{3}{8} \times \dfrac{2}{5} \times \dfrac{2}{3} =$

10. $\dfrac{1}{2} \times \dfrac{2}{3} \times \dfrac{3}{4} \times \dfrac{4}{5} =$

11. List the prime factors of 64.

12. List the prime factors of 81.

13. Reduce $\dfrac{32}{48}$ using the GCF.

14. Find the LCM of 24 and 36.

Find the same denominator and divide the numerators.

15. $\dfrac{2}{3} \div \dfrac{2}{7} =$

To divide, multiply by the reciprocal.

16. $\dfrac{2}{3} \div \dfrac{2}{7} =$

QUICK REVIEW

There are two ways to determine where to put the decimal in the answer, or product, when multiplying.

EXAMPLE 1

$$\begin{array}{r} .24 \\ .3 \\ \hline .072 \end{array}$$

Ignore the decimal point when multiplying, then think, "1/100 x 1/10 = 1/1000." The answer must be in thousandths and have three decimal places.

EXAMPLE 2

$$\begin{array}{r} .24 \\ .32 \\ \hline 48 \\ 72 \\ \hline .0768 \end{array}$$

Line up the decimal points when setting up the problem. After multiplying, count the total number of decimal places in the two factors and give the product the same number of decimal places as that total.

Multiply.

17. .7 x .3 =

18. 2.4 x 1.2 =

19. 1.3 x 2.1 =

20. .4 x 3.2 =

Use the correct order of operations to simplify. See Lesson 1A for review of negative numbers with exponents.

1. $-4^2 + (7 - 3)^2 - |-2| =$

2. $4(10 - 3) - 5(6) + 8 \div 2 =$

3. $-19 - (7)(-2) + 6^2 =$

4. $-(A - B) + A - B =$

5. $11^2 \div 4 + \dfrac{2}{3} =$

6. $5 \times 3 + 4^2 - 7 + (-8 \div 4) =$

7. $-5^2 + (-5)^2 =$

8. $|(9^2 \div 9) \div 3| =$

Solve.

9. $\dfrac{2}{5} \times \dfrac{7}{8} \times \dfrac{4}{7} =$

10. $\dfrac{5}{24} + \dfrac{9}{32} =$

Fill in the ovals with = (equals) or ≠ (is not equal to) and answer the questions.

11. (3 x 4) x 6 ◯ 3 x (4 x 6)

12. Is multiplication associative?

13. 10 - (8 - 6) ◯ (10 - 8) - 6

14. Is subtraction associative?

Find the same denominator and divide the numerators.

15. $1\frac{5}{7} \div 1\frac{3}{4} =$

To divide, multiply by the reciprocal.

16. $1\frac{5}{7} \div 1\frac{3}{4} =$

QUICK REVIEW

To divide decimals, first multiply both terms by the number that will make the divisor a whole number.

EXAMPLE 1

$.4\overline{)3.6}$ Multiply .4 and 3.6 by 10, then divide as usual. The decimal in the answer goes directly over the decimal below.

$4.\overline{)36.}^{\quad 9.}$

EXAMPLE 2 $.35\overline{)10.50}^{\quad 30.}$ Both .35 and 10.5 were multiplied by 100.

Divide. If necessary, add zeros and continue dividing until you find the answer to the nearest hundredth.

17. 2.3 ÷ .06 =

18. 2.5 ÷ .5 =

19. 2.5 : .05 –

20. 1.06 ÷ 5.3 =

Use the correct order of operations to simplify.

1. $-3 + 2^3 - 8 + 7^2 =$

2. $(5 \times 6) \div 3 =$

3. $[(10 + 3)^2 - 9] \div 20 =$

4. $A + B + 2A - 3B =$

5. $[42 \div 6 - 2] \times 11 =$

6. $8 + 45 \div 9 + 3 =$

7. $(-4)^2 + (5)^2 - 3^2 =$

8. $(192 \div 8) \times 4 - |67 - 200| =$

Solve.

9. $3\frac{1}{3} \times 1\frac{3}{4} \times \frac{7}{12} =$

10. $\frac{3}{7} + \frac{11}{13} =$

11. Reduce $\frac{30}{54}$ using the GCF.

12. Find the LCM of 10 and 100.

Fill in the oval with = (equals) or ≠ (is not equal to) and answer the question.

13. 6 + 2 + 9 $\bigcirc$ 2 + 6 + 9   14. Is addition commutative?

Divide.

15. $4\dfrac{5}{8} \div 2\dfrac{3}{4} =$ 16. 1.395 ÷ 3.1 =

17. $4\dfrac{2}{3} \div 1\dfrac{1}{4} =$ 18. .0016 ÷ .4 =

When dividing decimals, think of money to estimate your answer.

19. 1.2 ÷ .4 =

   (How many groups of 40¢ can I count out of $1.20?)

20. Divide $1.44 evenly among six people. How much would each receive?

These problems are designed to help you practice thinking skills and basic math skills.

1. How many composite numbers are there *between* 30 and 50?

2. List all of the factors of 289.

3. If 15 roses cost $18 and 15 carnations cost $10, what is the cost of one rose?

4. The plumber arrived and worked for 1.5 hours to fix the kitchen sink. His total bill was $75.78. This included $45.78 for parts and tax. What was the plumber's hourly charge for his labor?

5. A pool full of water has two pipes opening from it. One will empty 1/4 of the water in the pool in one hour and the other will empty 7/12 of the water in one hour. What part of the water will both pipes empty in one hour?

6. Joshua had 5/6 of a tank of gas when he started his trip. If he used 1/10 of what was there, what part of a tank was left at the end of the trip? If his gas tank holds 24 gallons when full, how many gallons were left in the tank at the end of the trip?

7. Bill can finish 3/5 of the job in 30 minutes. How long will it take him to do 1/5 of the job? How long will it take him to do 1/2 of the job?

Express each of the word problems using numerals, and then use the correct order of operations to simplify and find the answer to each.

8. Gary had 9 and bought 19. He divided his total amount evenly among himself and three other people. Then he bought 5 more. How many did Gary have then?

9. A square garden measures five yards on each side. A fence will go all around the square, except for a one-yard opening for a gate. Eight more yards of fence are needed to separate the front and back gardens. How many yards of fencing should be purchased?

10. Ida received a notice that her checking account was $20 overdrawn. (This means she had written checks for $20 more than was in her account.) She deposited $35. The next day she deposited twice that amount. Then she subtracted a $10 bank fee and wrote a check for $22.50. What should the balance in her checkbook show?

Simplify, then solve and check. The first one is done for you.

1. $-5A + 3 + 8A - 4 = 9 + 3 - 1$

$(-5A + 8A) + (3 - 4) = 9 + 3 - 1$

$$3A + (-1) = 11$$
$$ +1 \quad +1$$
$$\frac{3A}{3} = \frac{12}{3} \quad A = 4$$

2. $3B - B + 7 + 4B = 43$

3. $-4Y - 6 + 7Y + 3 + Y = 17$

4. $5Q + 3Q - 6 + 2Q = (2 + 3) + 9$

5. $6K - 5 + 4K - K + 2 = 12 \cdot 2$

6. $5C - 2C - 8 + 7 - C = 3 \cdot 4 + 1$

7. $4A + 6 = 2A + 12$

8. $10B - 2B + 3 = 5B + 21$

9. $6C - 8 + 3C = 7C - 2C + 12$

10. $6D - 10 = -2D - 34$

11. $-3A - 3 - 6A + 10A + 5 = 10$

12. $-5B - B + 4 + 10B - 7 = 7 \cdot 11$

13. $-4R + 7R - 3 + 5R = 10^2 - 7$

14. $-7Q + 8 - 6 + 5Q = 3 \cdot 5 - 7$

Simplify, then solve and check.

1. $-3A - 5 + 4A - 6 + 2A = 19$

2. $8B - 6 + 5B - 3 - 3B = 41$

3. $-5Y + 3 - 6Y + 2Y + 4 = 13$

4. $8Q - Q + 7 - 4 - 3Q = 7 + 4 \times 10$

5. $8M - 4M - 6 - 3 + 5M = 8^2 - 1$

6. $7C - 4C + 5 - 8 + C = 5^2 + 4$

7. $11A - 4A - 18 = 2A + A + 10$

8. $2B - 10B - 15 + 5 = 8B - 40 \quad 1B - 6$

9. $3C - 6 + 2C = 10C - 2C + 6$

10. $2D - 8 - 5D = -3D - 2D + 6$

11. $8K - 6 + 3K - 2K + 3 = 4 \times 33$

12. $B + B + B + 6 = 6B + 5 - 2B + 9$

13. $-2C + 12 = 2C - 6 + 6C - 12$

14. $10X - 3X - 9 + 3 - X = 51 \div 3 + 1$

Solve for the unknown.

1. $X + 3 = 9$

2. $X + 6 = 10$

3. $2X + 5 = 11$

4. $4Q - 2 = 10$

5. $4X + 2 = 2X + 8$

6. $3Y + 5 = 2Y + 7$

7. $Q + 4 = 3Q - 6$

8. $2R + 8 = 3R - 2$

Larger or smaller? (Use <, >, or = in the oval.)

9. $9 - 3 \bigcirc |4 - 11|$

10. $|1 - 2 - 3| \bigcirc |2 \cdot 3|$

Solve.

11. $(-3) \cdot 4 + 6^2 \cdot (-3) + 5^2 =$

12. $(14 - 9 + 2^2) - (3 \div 6 \cdot 2^2) =$

13. $\dfrac{4}{3} \times \dfrac{6}{10} \div \dfrac{2}{3} =$

14. $(.17)(.8) =$

15. (–8)(–7) =

16. (–4)^2 =

QUICK TIP

The least common multiple (LCM) is useful for simplifying some equations before solving.

EXAMPLE 1   Solve $\dfrac{3}{4}$ A + $\dfrac{1}{2}$ = $\dfrac{7}{10}$

4 = 2 x 2, 2 = 2, 10 = 2 x 5
So LCM = 2 x 2 x 5 = 20

Multiply each term by 20.

$$\overset{5}{(\cancel{20})}\dfrac{3}{\cancel{4}}A + \overset{10}{(\cancel{20})}\dfrac{1}{\cancel{2}} = \overset{2}{(\cancel{20})}\dfrac{7}{\cancel{10}}$$

15A + 10 = 14

A = 4/15

Use the LCM of the denominators to simplify before solving for the unknown.

17. $\dfrac{1}{2}$ + $\dfrac{2}{3}$ = $\dfrac{1}{4}$ X

18. $\dfrac{3}{5}$ X + $\dfrac{3}{4}$ = 1$\dfrac{1}{2}$

19. $\dfrac{1}{9}$ X + $\dfrac{2}{3}$ = $\dfrac{1}{5}$

20. $\dfrac{3}{8}$ – $\dfrac{1}{5}$ X = $\dfrac{3}{4}$

3D

Solve for the unknown.

1. $Y - 3 = 10$

2. $2B - 5 = 13$

3. $3C + 6 = -9$

4. $2D - 5 = 1$

5. $4E - 3 = -3$

6. $3X + 8 = -2X - 2$

7. $2Y - 2 = 3Y - 6$

8. $Z + 8 = 2Z + 18$

Larger or smaller? (Use <, >, or = in the oval.)

9. $|3 \times 2 \times (-2)|$ ◯ $24 \div (-3)$

10. $|17 - 3 - 20|$ ◯ $|7 + 0 + 1|$

Solve.

11. $[(6 - 2) \times 5^2 - 10] \div 5^2 =$

12. $(-7 - 6)^2 - (4 + 5 - 3)^2 =$

13. $\dfrac{5}{6} \times \dfrac{3}{7} \div \dfrac{2}{3} =$

14. How many groups of 12¢ are there in $1.68?

Use the answer to #15 to simplify #16, and then solve for X.

Hint: First make improper fractions.

15. Find the LCM of 2, 5, and 10.

16. $1\dfrac{1}{5}X + \dfrac{7}{10} = 2\dfrac{1}{2}X$

QUICK TIP

The LCM may also be used to simplify equations involving decimals.

EXAMPLE 1 Solve .05X − .35 = 2.7 If the decimals were written as fractions, the denominators would be 100 and 10. The LCM is 100.

Multiply each term by 100 → (100).05X − (100).35 = (100)2.7 → 5X − 35 = 270

X = 61

EXAMPLE 2   Solve .2X + 5 = 2.4
Multiply each term by 10 → (10).2X + (10)5 = (10)2.4
2X + 50 = 24 → X = −13

Use the LCM to make whole numbers before solving for the unknown.

17. .83 + .04X = .325

18. .18 + .2X = .17

19. .8X + 1.3 = 7 + .24

20. 8.2 − 4 = .08X

Solve for the unknown.

1. $-2X + 7 + 3X - 4 = 10 - 1$

2. $3Y + 8 - 2 - 2Y = 9 - 4 + 5$

3. $2X - 2 + 7 + X - X = 6 + 6 - 1$

4. $-2B + 3 + 5B + 1 = 2(3 + 2) + 9$

5. $3Q - 2 + Q = 3(2 + 2) - 2$

6. $5X + 5 - X - 3 = 3X - X + 4(2)$

7. $2Y - 4 + Y + 9 = -2Y - 4 + 4Y + 11$

8. $-4Q + 2 + 5Q + 2 = 3Q - 6$

Simplify using order of operations.

9. $(7 - 3)^2 \times |3 - 7| =$

10. $8 + (5 + 4)^2 \times 2 + 11^2 =$

11. $(4 \times 8 - 6 + 3^2) + (3 - 6 - 7^2 \times 3 + 4) =$

12. $(15 - 6 + 8^2 + 3 \div 3) - (10 + 9^2 - 40 \div 8) =$

Solve.

13. $\dfrac{3}{4} \times 2\dfrac{2}{3} \div 2 =$

14. $1.7 \times .8 =$

15. $(-19)(6) =$

16. $-6^2 =$

17. $-[-(-6)] =$

18. $-7 - (-3) =$

Use the LCM to simplify, then solve for the unknown.

19. $\dfrac{7}{8} + \dfrac{2}{3}X = \dfrac{1}{6}$

20. $.03X - .6 = .75$

Study the definitions of the terms used for different groups of numbers, and then answer the questions. The chart may help you see how each group is related to other groups.

Counting numbers (natural numbers) 1, 2, 3 . . .

Whole numbers   0, 1, 2, 3 . . .

Integers   . . . –3, –2, –1, 0, 1, 2, 3 . . .

Rational numbers   Can be written as a ratio or p/q. Remember that any integer can be written as p/1.

Irrational numbers   Non-repeating, non-terminating decimals. Examples are $\sqrt{2}$ and the value of π.

Real numbers   Both rational and irrational numbers together.

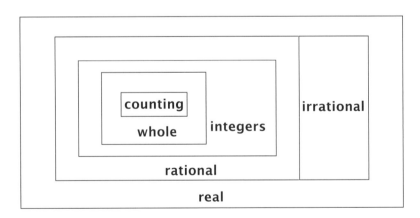

1. Are all integers also real numbers?

2. Is the square root of 16 a rational or irrational number?

3. Is –4 a rational or irrational number?

Missing information in a problem can be found by replacing the letters in a formula with known values and solving the resulting simple equation for the unknown value.

4. The formula for the area of a triangle is A = 1/2 bh. The area (A) of a certain triangle is 12 in^2 and the base (b) is six in. What is the height (h) of the triangle?

5. The formula for the perimeter of a rectangle is P = 2L + 2W. The perimeter (P) of a certain rectangle is 30 cm, and the length (L) is 10 cm. What is the width (W) of the rectangle?

6. The formula d = rt gives the distance (d) traveled if rate (r) and time (t) are known. John walked at the rate of 4 1/2 miles per hour for a distance of 11 1/4 miles. How many hours did John walk?

7. You can find the pressure below the surface of water by using the formula p = 0.433d. "p" stands for water pressure per square inch and "d" stands for the number of feet below the surface. If a diver's pressure gauge registers 43.3 pounds per square inch, how many feet below the surface is the diver?

Rewrite each expression using the distributive property. The first one is done for you.

1. 5(4 + 3) = 5(4) + 5(3)

2. 6(2 + 3 + 1) =

3. 7(A + B) =

4. 3(4C + 3B) =

5. 5(2X + 3Y – 3 + 4X) =

6. 8(A + 3B + 8 + 4A) =

Rewrite each expression using the distributive property in reverse. (Find the greatest common factor.) The first one is done for you.

7. 6X + 6Y = 6(X + Y)

8. 8A + 16B =

9. $14X + 21Y =$

10. $-2M - 6N =$

11. $6B + 18C =$

12. $15X + 10A =$

Simplify each equation using the greatest common factor, then solve for the unknown. The first one is done for you.

13. $5X + 15 = 45$
    $5(X + 3) = 5(9)$
    $X + 3 = 9$
    $X = 6$

14. $10X + 16 = 26$

15. $13Y - 26 + 39Y = 52$

16. $8A - 10 - 6A = 14$

17. $12X + 21 = 30$

18. $8X - 28 = 12$

Rewrite each expression using the distributive property.

1. 8(5 + 2) =

2. 5(4 − 3 + 2) =

3. 9(C + D) =

4. 5(2C + 4D) =

5. 3(X + Y + 4X) =

6. −2(3X + 2Y + Y) =

Rewrite each expression using the distributive property in reverse. (Find the GCF.)

7. 8X + 12Y = 4(+   )

8. −7X − 21Y =

9. $18A + 24B =$

10. $8X + 10 = 16$

11. $6A + 3 = 15$

12. $8A + 10 = 20$

Simplify each equation using the greatest common factor, then solve for the unknown.

13. $8X + 32 = 40$

14. $18Y + 27 = 45$

15. $15X - 10 + 5X = 25$

16. $9C - 6 - 12C = 18$

17. $14M - 42 + 56M = 28$

18. $6A - 16 - 4A = 20$

Distribute.

1. 4(A + B + 3) =

2. 5(X – Y + 6 + Z) =

3. 3(2Q – 4 + 3T + 7) =

4. 2(2X + 3Y – 5) =

Find the greatest common factor (reverse of distributing).

5. 15Y + 30X = 10

6. 12Q + 6Y = 15

7. 24Q + 18Y = 30

8. 36A – 14B = 10

Larger or smaller? (Use <, >, or = in the oval.)

9. 3 – 9 $\bigcirc$ |4 + 1²|

Divide by the greatest common factor (GCF) and solve for the unknown.

10. 4X – 16 = 24

11. 30 – 42Y = 18

12. $-24 + 56 = 16Q$

13. $-36 = 72A + 45$

14. Find the least common multiple (LCM) of 10 and 100.

15. Multiply this equation by the answer to #14 and solve:
    $.2X - .03 = .97$

16. Find the LCM of 3, 4, and 6.

17. Multiply this equation by the answer to #16 and solve: $\dfrac{3}{4} + \dfrac{1}{3}Q = \dfrac{5}{6}$

18. Find the LCM of 10 and 100.

19. Multiply this equation by the answer to #18 and solve:
    $-.7A + .8A = .12$

20. Divide 75.6 feet of fence by 4 to find the dimensions of a square garden enclosed by the fence.

Distribute.

1. $3(A - B - 2) =$

2. $5(3A - 9 + 2A) =$

3. $Q(X + 3) =$

4. $-(-A - B + 2C) =$

Find the greatest common factor (reverse of distributing).

5. $10X - 25Y = 40$

6. $24A + 12B = 36$

7. $-14Q - 21D = -42$

8. $3X + 4XY = 7X$

Divide by the greatest common factor (GCF) and solve for the unknown.

9. $22X + 33 = 44$

10. $7Q - 15 = 9 - 5Q$
    (*Hint:* First combine like terms.)

11. $30Y - 10 = 10$

12. $56B - 49 = 28$

13. Find the least common multiple (LCM) of 10 and 100.

14. Multiply this equation by the answer to #13 and solve:
    $.3X - 1.2 = .34$

15. Find the LCM of 4, 6, and 10.

16. Multiply this equation by the answer to #15 and solve: $-\dfrac{3}{4} + \dfrac{1}{6}R = \dfrac{7}{10}$

17. Gum balls are 5¢ apiece. How many can Zarah buy with $3.75?

QUICK REVIEW

A number may be expressed as a fraction, a decimal, or a percent.

EXAMPLE 1

Write $\dfrac{1}{2}$ as a decimal and a percent. $\quad \dfrac{1}{2} = \dfrac{50}{100} = .50 = 50\%$

Write 85% as a decimal and a fraction. $85\% = .85 = \dfrac{85}{100} = \dfrac{17}{20}$

Write 250% as a decimal and a fraction. $250\% = 2.50 = \dfrac{250}{100} = 2\dfrac{1}{2}$

Fill in the blanks.

18. $\dfrac{1}{4} = \dfrac{}{100} = .\underline{} = \underline{}\%$ 19. $40\% = .\underline{} = \dfrac{}{100} = \underline{}$

20. $125\% = \underline{} = \dfrac{}{100} = 1\underline{}$

Distribute.

1. $-2(Q + 2R - 3E) =$

2. $A^2(3 + B) =$

3. $-X(Y + 2 + M) =$

4. $-4(A^2 + B^2 + C^2) =$

Find the greatest common factor (reverse of distributing).

5. $4A - 16B = -18$

6. $20A - 40D = 100$

7. $6Q + 12G = 3$

8. $-5R - 15T = -20$

Solve.

9. $\dfrac{5}{6} \times 4 \div 2\dfrac{1}{2} =$

Divide by the GCF and solve for the unknown.

10. $-8 = -10C - 14$

11. $15 = -45M - 30$

12. $40 + 64 = 48N$

13. $63 = 35 - 7P$

14. Find the least common multiple (LCM) of 10 and 1000.

15. Multiply this equation by the answer to #14 and solve:
$.5Y - .3 = .002$

16. Find the LCM of 3, 4, and 12.

17. Multiply this equation by the answer to #16 and solve: $3\frac{2}{3} + \frac{5}{12}K = -1\frac{1}{4}$

Fill in the blanks.

18. $\frac{3}{4} = \frac{}{100} = .\underline{} = \underline{}\%$

19. $20\% = .\underline{} = \frac{}{100} = \underline{}$

20. $380\% = \underline{} = \frac{}{100} = 3\underline{}$

Graphs provide a way to organize information.

Study the line and bar graphs and answer the questions.

A factory has two different kinds of machines for making widgets. Machine A started at the beginning of the work day. Machine B started two hours late because it needed to be repaired.

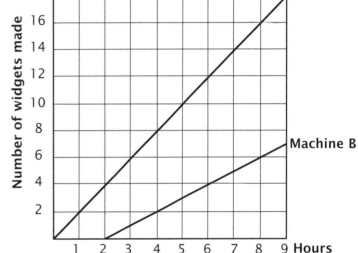

1. How many widgets did Machine A make each hour?

2. How many widgets had Machine A made after nine hours?

3. How many widgets did Machine B make each hour?

4. How many widgets had Machine B made six hours after the start of the work day?

5. If Machine B had been ready to start at the beginning of the work day and worked at its same rate, how many widgets could it have made in nine hours?

This bar graph shows John's and David's scores on their history tests for the first five tests of the year. Besides using graphs to get factual information, you can make deductions about the reasons for the data. Be careful to remember that these deductions are only guesses. Estimate scores as closely as possible when answering the questions.

6. On which test did John and David get the same score?

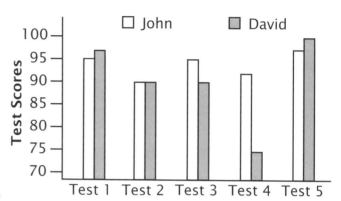

7. On which test did David get the lowest of all his scores?

8. What is the difference between David's highest and lowest scores?

9. Which boy had the highest average test score?

Two graphs that show the same data can be arranged differently and give very different impressions. The graphs below were drawn by two car salesmen to show the boss their sales for the previous month.

10. How many cars did each man sell? Do the graphs agree?

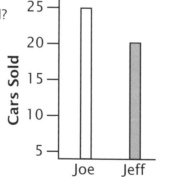
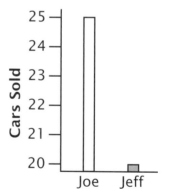

11. Which man do you suspect drew each graph?

12. Record your own data and make a graph. Then make a second graph with the same data that gives a different impression of the facts.

Follow the directions for each graph.

1. Write the coordinates of point A.

2. In what quadrant is point A?

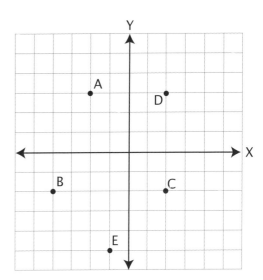

3. Write the coordinates of point B.

4. In what quadrant is point B?

5. Write the coordinates of point C.

6. In what quadrant is point C?

7. Write the coordinates of point D.

8. In what quadrant is point D?

9. Write the coordinates of point E.

10. In what quadrant is point E?

11. Graph and label point F. (−3, 5)

12. In what quadrant is point F?

13. Graph and label point H. (4, 6)

14. In what quadrant is point H?

15. Graph and label point J. (5, −3)

16. In what quadrant is point J?

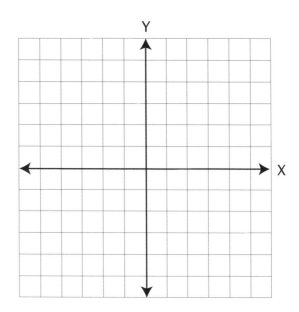

17. Descartes developed the Cartesian coordinate system to show algebra _____.

18. In the fourth quadrant, X is _____ and Y is _____.

19. Graph (5, 2), (5, −1), and (5, 5). What do these have in common?

20. If you draw a line through these points, it has a(n) _____ coordinate of _____.

21. Plot all the odd numbers between −5 and 4.

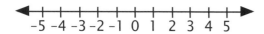

22. Plot all the values between and including 0 and 3.

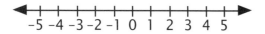

23. Plot all the values of X ≥ 0.

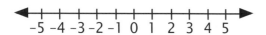

24. Plot all the values of X ≤ −π.

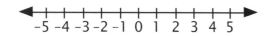

Follow the directions for each graph.

1. Write the coordinates of point K.

2. In what quadrant is point K?

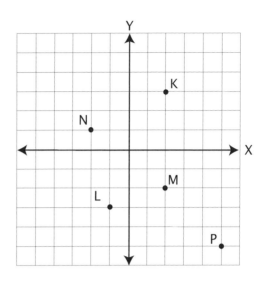

3. Write the coordinates of point L.

4. In what quadrant is point L?

5. Write the coordinates of point M.

6. In what quadrant is point M?

7. Write the coordinates of point N.

8. In what quadrant is point N?

9. Write the coordinates of point P.

10. In what quadrant is point P?

11. Graph and label point Q. (–5, –1)

12. In what quadrant is point Q?

13. Graph and label point R. (6, 3)

14. In what quadrant is point R?

15. Graph and label point S. (4, –2)

16. In what quadrant is point S?

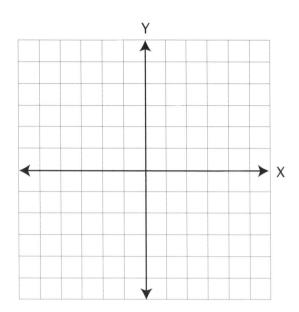

17. What are the coordinates of the origin?

18. In the third quadrant, X is _____ and Y is _____.

19. Graph (5, –2), (2, –2), and (0, –2). What do these have in common?

20. If you draw a line through these points, it has a(n) _____ coordinate of _____.

21. Plot all the values of X > –2 3/4.

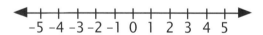

22. Plot all the values of X ≤ 1.7.

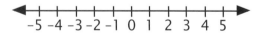

23. Plot all the values of X > 3.9.

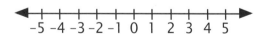

24. Plot all the values of X < 4.

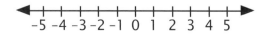

Write the coordinates of the following points.

1. Point A (___ , ___)

2. Point B (___ , ___)

3. Point C (___ , ___)

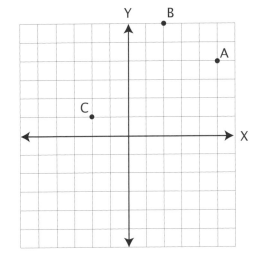

Graph and label.

4. Point D (1, –4)

5. Point E (6, –6)

6. Point F (0, 0)

7. René _____ developed the graph to show algebra geometrically.

8. In the first quadrant, X is _____ and Y is _____.

9. Every point along the X–axis is (something, 0) because X changes but ___ equals 0.

   Every point along the Y–axis is (0, something) because Y changes but ___ equals 0.

10. The point (0, 0) is called the _____.

Simplify and solve for the unknown.

11. .05 X + .12X = .85

12. −72 + 8Y = 32

13. 7(−B + 2 + 7 − 1) = 13 + 3B + 5B

14. −4(P − 6) + 2P = |5 − 3 + 6|

15. $2\frac{4}{7} - \frac{1}{4}Q = -5\frac{2}{3}$

16. .3X − .06X = 1.25

17. What are the prime factors of 116?

18. What are the prime factors of 36?

19. According to the commutative property,
     A + B is the same as _____.

20. According to the associative property,
     (A + B) + C is the same as _____.

Write the coordinates of the following points.

1. Point A (___ , ___)

2. Point B (___ , ___)

3. Point C (___ , ___)

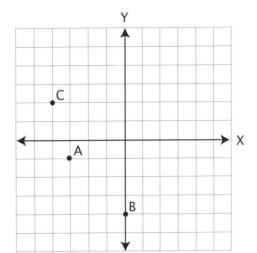

Graph and label.

4. Point D (5, 2)

5. Point E (3, –2)

6. Point F (–2, 1)

7. The _____ coordinate system is named after René Descartes.

8. In the second quadrant, X is _____ and Y is

_____ .

9. Graph (3, 6) , (3, 4), and (3, –4) on the graph above. What do all these points have in common?

10. If you connect all the points in #9, every point along this line has a(n) ____ coordinate of ____.

Simplify and solve for the unknown.

11. –1.3 + 2.7 = .2Y

12. 17Q – 14XQ = 11Q (Solve for X.)

Simplify and solve for the unknown.

13. D(3 − 7) − 12 = 0

14. $(6^2 \div 9) \times 2 - 9Y = 8(Y - 4 + 9)$

15. $4\frac{1}{2} = 1\frac{1}{4}R + 2\frac{3}{7}$

16. .35P + 3.2 = −4P

Fill in the blanks.

17. $75\% = .\underline{\quad} = \dfrac{\quad}{100} = \underline{\quad}$

18. $113\% = \underline{\quad} = \dfrac{\quad}{100} = 1\underline{\quad}$

19. $\dfrac{2}{5} = \dfrac{\quad}{100} = .\underline{\quad} = \underline{\quad}\%$

20. According to the distributive property, A(B + B) is the same as _____ .

Write the coordinates of the following points.

1. Point A (___, ___)

2. Point B (___, ___)

3. Point C (___, ___)

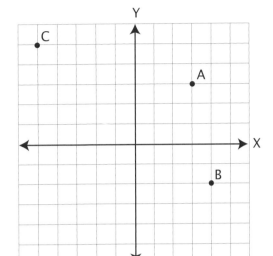

Graph and label.

4. Point D (–1, –4)

5. Point E (–5, 3)

6. Point F (2, –1)

7. _____ geometry is geometry used to analyze algebraic equations.

8. In the third quadrant, X is _____ and Y is

_____ .

9. Graph (–2, 0) , (–2, 6), and (–2, –3) on the graph above. What do all these points have in common?

10. If you connect all the points in #9, every point along this line has a(n) _____ coordinate of _____.

Simplify and solve for the unknown.

11. $1.08V = .7 - .24$

12. $9X^2M = 10X^2 - 19X^2$ (Solve for M.)

Simplify and solve for the unknown.

13. $(11 - 4)^2 \div 7 - |3 - 9| = 14(R + 3R - 2R + 1)$

14. $6[\, 8 - (Y + 4)\,] = 3[(10 + 1)^2 - (7 - 5 + 4)\,]$

15. $3\frac{1}{8} - 1\frac{4}{7} = 1\frac{1}{2}D$

16. $-1.203H + .9 = -.6$

QUICK REVIEW

Any fraction may be expressed as a decimal if you recall that the line in the fraction means "divide."

EXAMPLE 1   Write $\frac{5}{6}$ as a decimal.

$$\begin{array}{r} .833 \\ 6\,\overline{\smash{)}5.00} \\ \underline{48} \\ 20 \\ \underline{18} \\ 20 \end{array}$$

This may be written as .8$\overline{3}$, since the 3 will repeat indefinitely. Sometimes the directions will ask you to round to hundredths or thousandths.

Write as a decimal. Round to the hundredths place.

17. $\frac{1}{8}$ 18. $\frac{2}{3}$

19. $\frac{3}{5}$ 20. $\frac{2}{9}$

A vector is a mathematical concept that has two dimensions: direction and magnitude (size or distance). Suppose an ant is sitting on a hill. If the ant goes three steps directly towards the north (due north), the ant has a direction (north) and a magnitude (three steps). North and east are considered positive directions, and south and west are considered negative directions. Think of two number lines turned at right angles to each other.

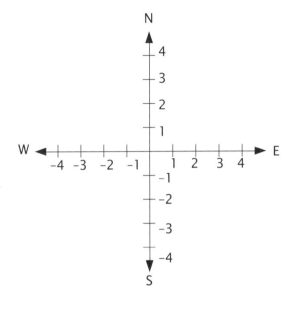

Suppose the ant traveled north three steps and then turned around and walked five steps south. What would be the result?

3 + (–5) = –2, so the ant would be two steps south of its starting point.

Use your pencil to trace the ant's journey on the number lines.

We can say that the ant's first vector was (three steps, north) and its second vector was (five steps, south). When we add the two vectors, we get the resultant vector, which is (two steps, south). It is the combination of the ant's two journeys, and tells how it could have gotten to the same place in only one journey.

You will learn more about vectors in future math courses and use them in science courses, such as physics.

Follow the directions.

1. Another ant begins its journey from the same ant hill, which we can call the origin, and goes six steps due east. Describe its vector by giving magnitude and direction.

2. The ant in #1 continues its journey and goes 10 steps due west. Describe the resultant vector for the entire journey. Remember, the resultant tells how far, and in what direction, to go in order to get to the end point in a single journey.

3.   Several children at a birthday party are going on a treasure hunt. The instructions are given in vectors as follows: Go three paces north, four paces west, seven paces south, and then four paces east. The treasure is at the location of the resultant vector. Give the resultant vector. You may use a pencil to trace the journey on the number lines.

Vectors can be drawn using arrows. The head of the arrow points in the direction of the motion. Usually a number is placed along the line of the arrow to show the magnitude.

Add and subtract to find the resultant vector.

4.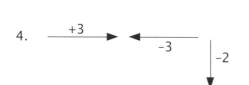

5.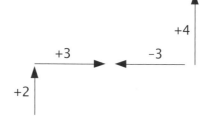

You can find the magnitude of some vectors using the Pythagorean theorem.

Leave your answer with a radical sign, or use your calculator to simplify it.

6.   Jack drove four miles due east and then four miles due north to the store. How far is the store from the starting point?

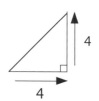

7.   The resultant vector in #6 has a direction halfway between north and east. We call it northeast. Describe the resultant vector using magnitude and direction.

8.   Sally drove eight miles south and eight miles west. Describe the resultant vector using magnitude and direction.

Follow the directions for each graph.

1. Bud's Bakery had two loaves of bread in stock. Bud can bake three loaves of bread every hour. Fill in the blanks.

Hours	Loaves
_____	_____
_____	_____
_____	_____
_____	_____

2. Plot the points and connect them.

3. Write an equation for the line.

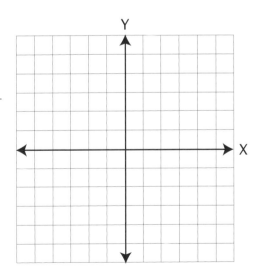

4. Fred's Sporting Goods had three back orders for stringing tennis rackets. Fred could string two rackets each hour. Fill in the blanks.

Hours	Rackets
_____	_____
_____	_____
_____	_____
_____	_____

5. Plot the points and connect them.

6. Write an equation for the line.

7. Bill had one steak barbecued for the picnic. As the guests arrived, Bill began to barbecue four steaks each hour. Fill in the blanks.

Hours	Steaks
_____	_____
_____	_____
_____	_____
_____	_____

8. Plot the points and connect them.

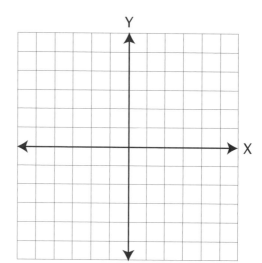

9. Write an equation for the line.

10. $Y = 2X - 1$. Using this information, fill in the table.

X	Y
_____	_____
_____	_____
_____	_____
_____	_____

11. Plot the points and connect them.

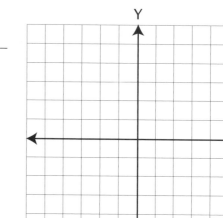

12. Write a word problem that fits the graph.

Follow the directions for each graph.

1. The bulb was planted six cm deep. It grew two cm a week. Fill in the blanks.

2. Plot the points and connect them.

Weeks	cm
_____	_____
_____	_____
_____	_____
_____	_____

3. Write an equation for the line.

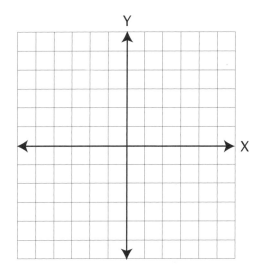

4. In the fishing contest, Bill was five fish behind his opponent. During the final part of the contest, Bill caught three fish per hour and his opponent caught none. Fill in the blanks.

Hours	Fish
_____	_____
_____	_____
_____	_____
_____	_____

5. Plot the points and connect them.

6. Write an equation for the line.

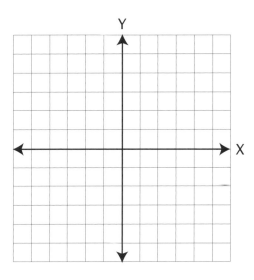

7. When we arrived at the race, Lori was five meters behind her opponent. Then she gained two meters every second thereafter.

Fill in the blanks.

Seconds	Meters
_____	_____
_____	_____
_____	_____
_____	_____

8. Plot the points and connect them.

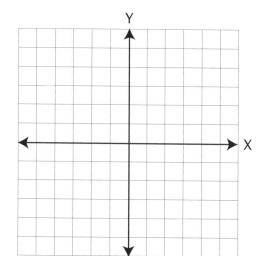

9. Write an equation for the line.

10. $Y = 3X - 4$. Use this information, to fill in the table.

X	Y
_____	_____
_____	_____
_____	_____

11. Plot the points and connect them.

12. Write a word problem that fits the graph.

Follow the directions for each graph.

1. Abraham Lincoln was on a speaking tour. He made one speech in Illinois before he left. After that he spoke twice a day. Fill in the first table below the graph.

2. Plot these points and connect them.

3. Write an equation for the line.
(Speeches = ___ per Day + ___ in Illinois)

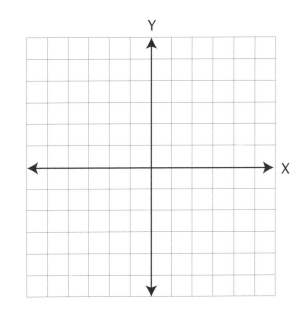

4. From the beginning, J. S. Bach composed two masterpieces per year. Show the first three years on the second table.

5. Plot these points and connect them.

6. Write an equation for the line.

Day	Speeches
0	1
1	3
___	___
___	___

Year	Master
0	0
1	2
___	___
___	___

7. Plot the point (4, 5) and tell in which quadrant it is contained.

8. Plot the point (–4, 6) and tell in which quadrant it is contained.

9. Draw a line where X = 5.

10. Draw a line where X = –2.

Simplify and solve for the unknown.

11. 63A – 81 = 72

12. 48 + 54X = 36

13. $[-5^2 - (-5)^2] \cdot 3 + 100 = 10X - 3X - 2X$

14. .01 – .1 + .5 = 2Y

15. $\dfrac{2}{A} - \dfrac{5}{A} = \dfrac{X}{A}$

(A ≠ 0. The unknown must be limited because a fraction indicates division, and it is not possible to divide by zero.)

16. $2\dfrac{1}{2}X + \dfrac{2}{3}X = 1\dfrac{5}{6}$

17. Write $\dfrac{5}{8}$ as a decimal.

18. Distribute: X(X + Y + 2Q) =

QUICK TIP

Read word problems carefully before expressing them in algebraic terms.

EXAMPLE 1   A number times two, plus four, and the sum is squared.

This is written as $(2N + 4)^2$. (You may use any letter for the unknown. Our answers will use "N" unless specified otherwise.)

Choose the correct algebraic expression of each word problem.

19. The opposite of a number, plus 6; the sum times 5.

A. (–N + 6)5   or   B. (N – 6) ÷ 5

20. Twice a number, less 7, plus the number, equals 1/2 the number.

A. 2(N – 7) – N = 1/2 N   or   B. 2N – 7 + N = 1/2 N

Follow the directions for each graph.

1. During class I didn't get any homework finished. That evening I was able to do three pages per hour. Fill in the first table below the graph.

2. Plot these points and connect them.

3. Write an equation for the line.

   (Pages = ___ per Hour + ___ in class)

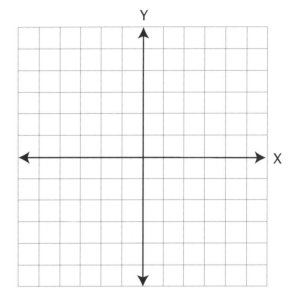

4. While the customers were coming in, I cooked three eggs. After that I cooked two eggs per customer. Fill in the second table.

5. Plot these points and connect them.

Hours	Pages
0	0
1	3
___	___
___	___

Cust.	Eggs
0	3
1	5
___	___
___	___

6. Write an equation for the line.

7. Plot the point (–6, 4) and tell in which quadrant it is contained.

8. Plot the point (6, –3) and tell in which quadrant it is contained.

9. Draw a line where X = 4.

10. Draw a line where X = –1.

Simplify and solve for the unknown.

11. $-6(Y - 5 + 9) + 7(2Y + 9) = -1$

12. $3X + 3 - X - 8 + 5X + 12 = 4X - 12 - 6X + 10$

13. $-5R + |\, 9^2 - 3^2 \,| + 13 = 7R + 5R$ 14. $[\, 8 - (-2) \,]^2 = 10X$

15. $\dfrac{Y}{2A} - \dfrac{4}{A} = \dfrac{1}{2A}$ if $A \neq 0$ 16. $2\dfrac{3}{5}D - \dfrac{3}{8}D = 4\dfrac{7}{10}$

17. Write $\dfrac{11}{12}$ as a decimal.   18. Use GCF to simplify if $X^2Y \neq 0$:
$$X^2Y - 4X^2Y + BX^2Y = 0$$

19. A number squared divided by three times two minus ten.
A. $(N \div 3)^2 \times 2 - 10$ or   B. $N^2 \div 3 \times 2 - 10$

20. Distribute: $A(A - B + 2AB) =$

Follow the directions for each graph.

Minutes	Burgers
0	3
1	4
2	5
3	6

1. When I arrived at work at MacBurger there were _____ burgers on the grill. I could cook an average of _____ per minute. Fill in the blanks from the data in the table on the right.

2. Plot these points and connect them.

3. Write an equation for the burgers. (Burgers = _____ per minute + _____ on griddle)

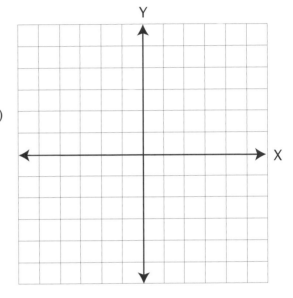

Use the equation Y = X + 2 for #4–6.

4. Fill in the table below the graph.

5. Plot the points and connect them.

6. Make a story to fit the equation.

X	Y
____	____
____	____
____	____
____	____

7. Plot the point (0, 4) and tell on which axis it is located.

8. Plot the point (4, 0) and tell on which axis it is located.

9. Draw a line where Y = 1.

10. Draw a line where Y = -4.

Simplify and solve for the unknown.

11. $4AB - 7A = 15A$

12. $7(B + 6 - 2B - 4) = 3^2(-4B - 8 - 9 + 2B)$

13. $-3(3G + 5G) + |3 - 12| = 18G + 5(-G - 4)$

14. $-1.2 + .07X = .3$

15. $\frac{3}{10} - 1\frac{3}{5} = -\frac{5}{8}M$

16. $\frac{5}{9}X - 2\frac{5}{6} = \frac{7}{10}$

17. Write $\frac{2}{7}$ as a decimal (round to hundredths).

18. Write 35% as a decimal and as a fraction.

19. Rewrite using algebraic symbols: The opposite of a number, times the opposite of four; that product divided by the product of two times five.

20. Rewrite using algebraic symbols: Three times a number, minus the number, plus twice the number, plus seven.

Here are some fun activities to help you become more familiar with the Cartesian coordinate system.

Follow the directions for each one.

1. Plot each set of points, and then connect the points in that set to make a square or rectangle. When you have finished connecting the points, shade the inside of each shape with your pencil. What have you drawn?

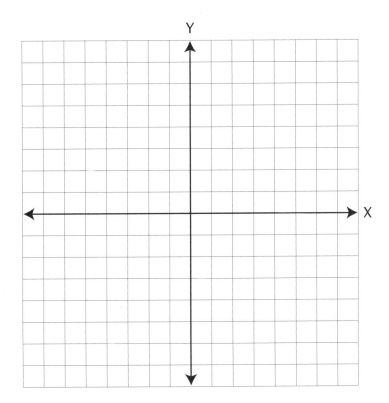

a. (2, 7), (2, 8), (6, 7), (6, 8)

b. (3, 4), (3, 6), (5, 4), (5, 6)

c. (1, −1), (1, 4), (−1, −1), (−1, 4)

d. (−3, 4), (−3, 6), (−5, 4), (−5, 6)

e. (−2, 7), (−2, 8), (−6, 7), (−6, 8)

f. (2, −1), (2, −2), (−2, −1), (−2, −2)

g. (4, −3), (4, −5), (5, −3), (5, −5)

h. (−4, −3), (−4, −5), (−5, −3), (−5, −5)

i. (4, −4), (4, −5), (−4, −4), (−4, −5)

2. Plot the first two points, and then draw a line connecting those two points. Continue to plot each point, and connect it to the last one you plotted. What have you drawn?

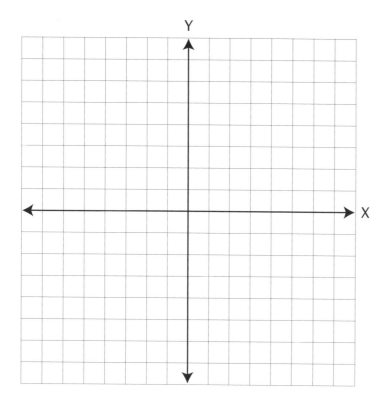

a. (–9, 7)	m. (–1, –7)	y. (6, 3)
b. (–9, –6)	n. (–1, –6)	z. (3, 3)
c. (–8, –6)	o. (0, –6)	z. (3, 6)
d. (–8, –7)	p. (0, –7)	aa. (4, 8)
e. (–7, –8)	q. (1, –8)	bb. (0, 8)
f. (–6, –8)	r. (2, –8)	cc. (1, 6)
g. (–5, –7)	s. (3, –7)	dd. (1, 3)
h. (–5, –6)	t. (3, –6)	ee. (–3, 3)
i. (–4, –6)	u. (5, –6)	ff. (–3, 7)
j. (–4, –7)	v. (5, –7)	gg. (–9, 7)
k. (–3, –8)	w. (9, –7)	
l. (–2, –8)	x. (6, –3)	

Fill in the blanks.

1. The point where a line crosses the Y-axis is known as the

    Y _____ .

2. Slope may be written as the _____ dimension divided by
    the _____ dimension.

3. A line with a _____ slope slants down to the right.

For each graph, tell whether the slope is positive or negative, then make a triangle and find *m*.

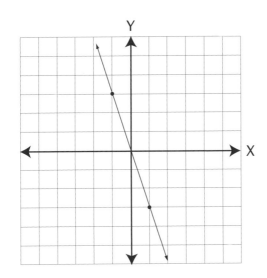   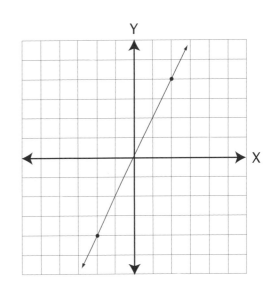

4. positive or negative? _____   5. positive or negative? _____

    m = ____   m = ____

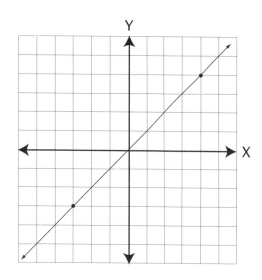

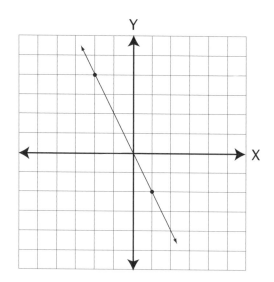

6. positive or negative? _____

m = _____

7. positive or negative? _____

m = _____

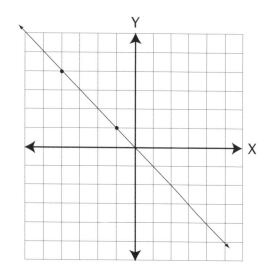

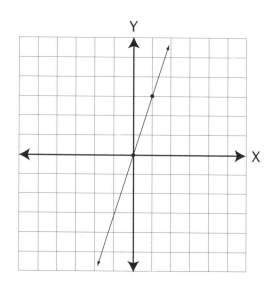

8. positive or negative? _____

m = _____

9. positive or negative? _____

m = _____

Fill in the blanks.

1.   In the formula Y = 4X + 5, the slope is _____ .

2.   In the formula Y = −X + 3, the Y−intercept is _____ .

3.   Parallel lines have the same _____ .

For each graph, tell whether the slope is positive or negative, and then make a triangle and find m.

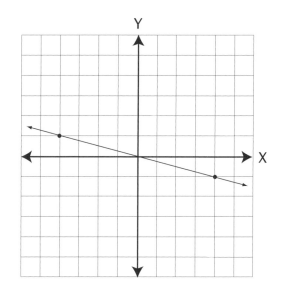
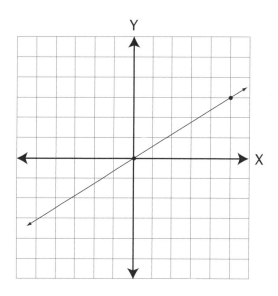

4. positive or negative? _____

5. positive or negative? _____

m = ____

m = ____

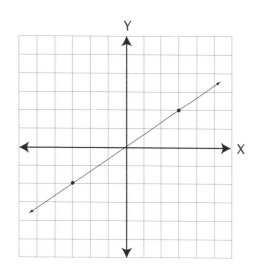

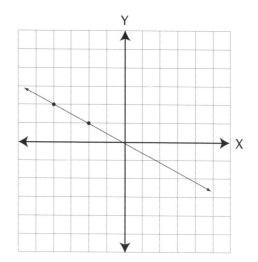

6. positive or negative? _____

   m = ____

7. positive or negative? _____

   m = ____

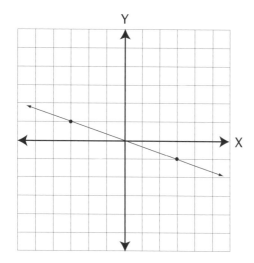

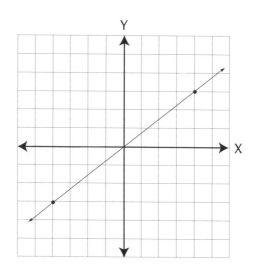

8. positive or negative? _____

   m = ____

9. positive or negative? _____

   m = ____

SYSTEMATIC REVIEW

Fill in the blanks.

1 A line that includes the point (0, –3) has a Y-intercept of _____ .

2. A line with a negative slope slants _____ to the right.

Find the slope and intercept of each line, and then write the slope–intercept formula for the line.

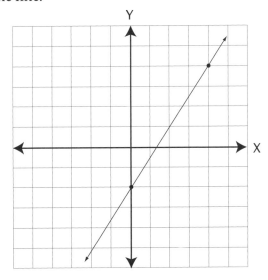

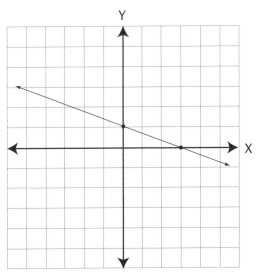

3. m = _____   b = ____

5. m = _____   b = ____

4. Y = _____

6. Y = _____

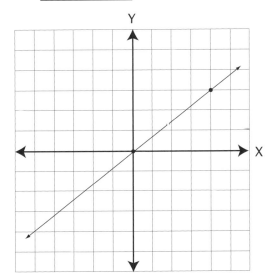

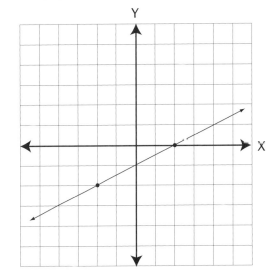

7. m = _____   b = ____

9. m = _____   b = ____

8. Y = _____

10. Y = _____

ALGEBRA 1   SYSTEMATIC REVIEW 7C

11. Plot all the values of X > –3.5.

12. Plot all the values of X ≤ 1 1/2.

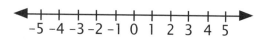

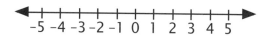

Simplify.

13. $[(7 – 3) \times 4^2 – 9] \div 3^3 =$

14. $|-4 – 2| + 8^2 – 7 \times 5 + 19 =$

15. $13^2 + 5 \div 10 =$

16. $5(9 – 2) – 6(7) + 2^3 \cdot 3 =$

Solve.

17. $2X – 5 = –X + 13$

18. $Y + 14 – 3Y = 0$

19. $-3\,1/2\,B + 2/3 = 5\,1/4 + 5/6\,B$

20. $2.7T + 1.09 = 5.3 – .6T$

Fill in the blanks.

1. In the formula Y = 4X + 5, the slope is _____ .

2. In the formula Y = -X + 3, the Y-intercept is _____ .

Find the slope and intercept of each line, and then write the slope–intercept formula for the line.

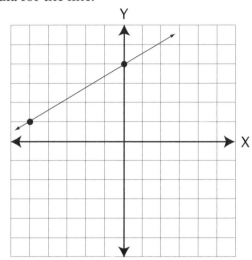
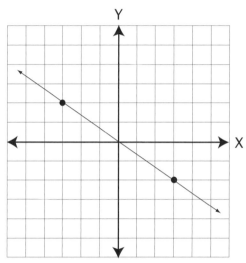

3. m = _____ b = ____

4. Y = _____

5. m = _____ b = ____

6. Y = _____

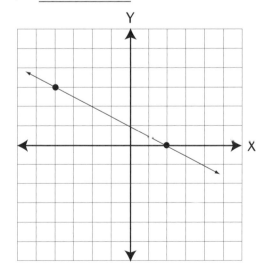
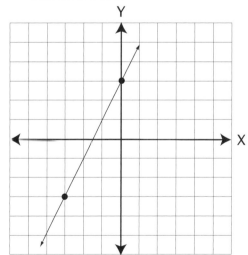

7. m = _____ b = ____

8. Y = _____

9. m = _____ b = ____

10. Y = _____

11. Plot all the values of X = –2.

12. Plot all the odd values of X between –4 and 4.

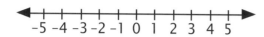

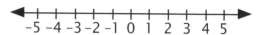

Simplify.

13. $-|\,5 - 8\,| \times 4 - 7 + 12 =$

14. $-7^2 \times 2 - 48 + 5 =$

15. $144 \div 9 \times 3 - |100 - 121| =$

16. $8\,[17 - 3 \times 2] + 6^2 - (-5)^2 =$

Solve.

17. $4A + 11 = A - 4$

18. $-5F = -6F + 8$

19. $\dfrac{2}{5} - \dfrac{1}{6}D = -\dfrac{3}{4}$

20. $.03M - 1.2 = -.48M$

Fill in the blank.

1. A line with a positive slope slants _____ to the right.

2. Parallel lines have the same _____ .

Find the slope and intercept of each line, and then write the slope–intercept formula for the line.

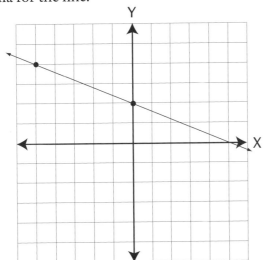
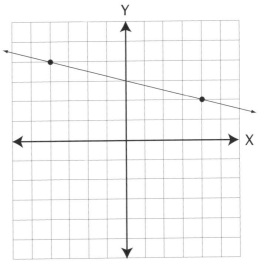

3. m = _____   b = _____

4. Y = _____

5. m = _____   b = _____

6. Y = _____

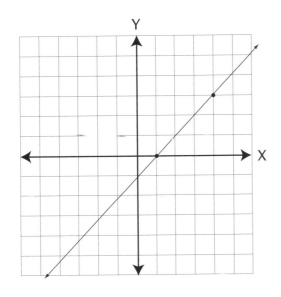
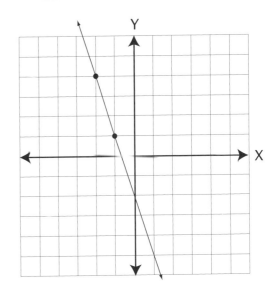

7. m = _____   b = _____

8. Y = _____

9. m = _____   b = _____

10. Y = _____

11. Plot all the values of $X \geq 2$.

12. Plot all the values of $X < 0$.

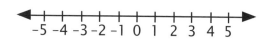

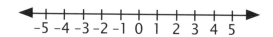

Simplify.

13. $11 \cdot 3^2 - 14 \times 2 =$

14. $2 \cdot 7 + 4^2 - 15 =$

15. $(-6)^2 + (8 - 3^2) =$

16. $16 \div 8 \cdot 5 - 14 =$

Solve.

17. $-2B + 5 - 3 + B = B - 4B + 1 - 10$

18. $5K + 6 - K - 9 = -2K + 6 + 3K - 3$

19. $4\ 3/10 = -2/3 + 8/9\ G$

20. $-5 - .6R = -9.8$

ALGEBRA 1

Once you understand the concepts of slope and intercept, you can estimate the formula for a line when only the X- and Y-axes are shown. There are three questions you must answer:

1. Is the slope of the line positive or negative?

2. Approximately where does the line cross the Y-axis (the Y-intercept)?

3. How steep is the line (the slope)?

Match each line with the equation that best describes it. The first two are done for you.

1. Y = −4X   t

2. Y = X + 3   s

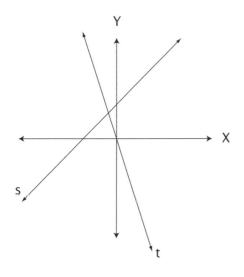

Examine line *s*. It goes up to the right, so the slope is positive. The slope is about halfway between the horizontal X-axis and the vertical Y-axis, so it is close to one. The Y-intercept is a short distance above the origin, so three is a reasonable value for the intercept.
The best equation for line *s* is #2: Y = X + 3.

Examine line *t*. It goes down to the right, so the slope is negative. The slope is steeper than one, and four is a good estimate. The Y-intercept is at the origin, so its value is zero.
The best equation for line *t* is #1: Y = −4X.

3. $Y = -1/2 X + 1$ ___

4. $Y = 2X + 1$ ___

5. $Y = 1/2 X - 1$ ___

6. $Y = 2X$ ___

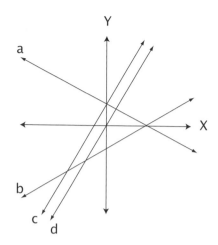

7. $Y = 3X$ ___

8. $Y = 1/4 X + 3$ ___

9. $Y = X$ ___

10. $Y = -X - 3$ ___

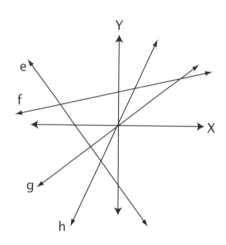

Identify the slope and intercept of each equation. Then draw the line corresponding to the equation.

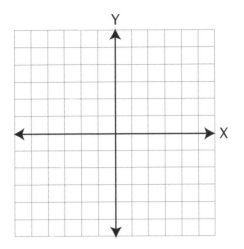

1. Y = 1/4 X – 2

    m = _____

    b = _____

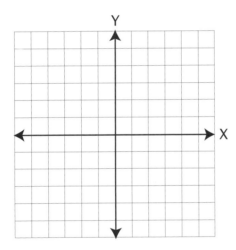

2. Y = –X + 2

    m = _____

    b = _____

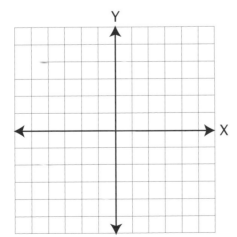

3. Y = –2

    m = _____

    b = _____

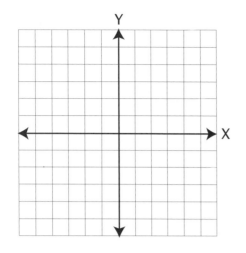

4. Y = 3/5 X + 1

    m = _____

    b = _____

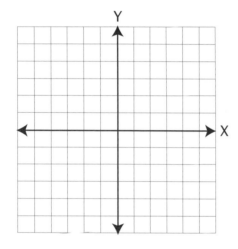

5. Y = X

    m = _____

    b = _____

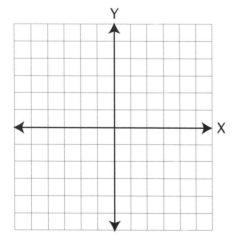

6. X = –3

    m = _____

    b = _____

Identify the slope and intercept of each equation.
Then draw the line corresponding to the equation.

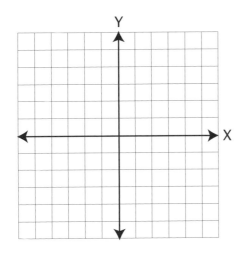

1. Y = –2X – 5

    m = _____

    b = _____

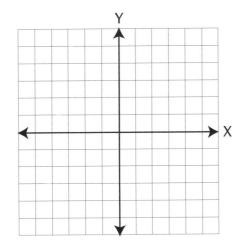

2. Y = –3/2 X

    m = _____

    b = _____

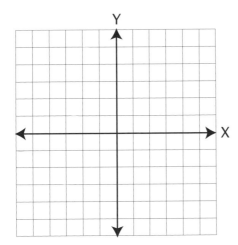

3. X = 0

    m = _____

    b = _____

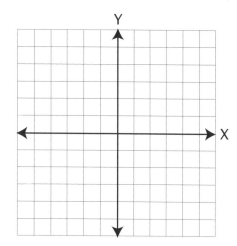

4. Y = -3X + 2

    m = _____

    b = _____

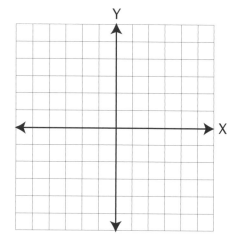

5. Y = 2X - 1

    m = _____

    b = _____

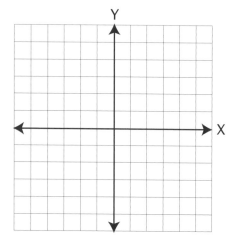

6. Y = 4

    m = _____

    b = _____

1. Joey borrowed four dollars to open a video store. He lost one dollar each day. Fill in the table on the right.

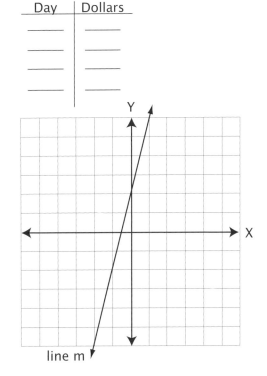

line m

Day	Dollars
___	___
___	___
___	___
___	___

2. Plot these points and connect them.

3. Write an equation for the line.

(Dollars = ___ per Day – ___ borrowed)

4. Given: Y = –2X.
   This time Joey started with ____ dollar(s) and lost ____ dollars each day.
   Use the table under the graph.

5. Graph the points and the line.

Day	Dollars
___	___
___	___
___	___
___	___

6. The slope is ____ and the intercept is ____ .

7. Estimate the slope and intercept of line *m* on the graph.

8. What would the equation of the line be using the slope–intercept formula?

9. This line is graphed within which quadrants?

10. Graph Y = –2 and label it line *g*.

Simplify and solve for the unknown.

11. 60R – 90R = 70

12. –18 + 54X = 27

13. $[(6 + 5)^2 – 1] \div 12 = 3X + |-2X|$
X is positive

14. 4B – 32B = 36B – 8BY (4B ≠ 0)

15. 1.03 – .8Y = 5

16. $3\frac{3}{4}Y = 2\frac{1}{5} + 3\frac{5}{6}$

17. 5X – 20 = 50X + 35

18. $\frac{3}{10}X - 3\frac{1}{6}X = 4\frac{1}{4}$

QUICK REVIEW

"What fraction of 6 is 3?" is written as WF x 6 = 3.

EXAMPLE   Write an equation and solve: What fraction of 10 is 5?
WF x 10 = 5   Solving for the unknown :

$$\frac{1}{10}(WF \times 10) = \frac{1}{10}(5) \rightarrow WF = \frac{5}{10} = \frac{1}{2}$$

19. Write an equation and solve:
What fraction of 7 is 5?

20. Write an equation and solve:
What fraction of 5 is 2?

1. T. Turner borrowed three dollars to open a TV network. He lost two dollars each day. Fill in the table on the right.

Day	Dollars
___	___
___	___
___	___
___	___

2. Plot these points and connect them.

3. Write an equation for the line.

(Dollars = ___ per day – ___ borrowed)

4. Given: Y = 3X + 2.
   This time T. T. started with ____ dollars and made ____ dollars each day.
   Use the table below the graph.

5. Graph the points and the line.

6. The slope is ____ and the intercept is ____ .

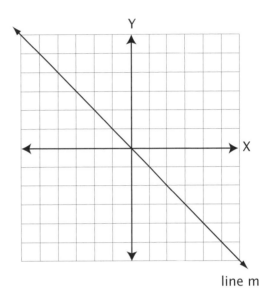

line m

Day	Dollars
___	___
___	___
___	___
___	___

7. Estimate the slope and intercept of line *m* on the graph.

8. What would the equation of the line be using the slope–intercept formula?

9. This line is graphed within which quadrants?

10. Graph Y = 0 and label it line *g*.

Simplify and solve for the unknown.

11. $12Y = 6 - 24$

12. $-72 + 60F = 48$

13. $2^2[5(4 - 2X + 3) - 3(8 + 9X - 4X)] = 0$

14. $-50BY + 30B = 80BY - 40B$ $(B \neq 0)$

15. $.018 = .25Q + 2.04$

16. $-1\frac{5}{8}M + 4\frac{1}{3} = 1\frac{1}{6}$

17. $-1.3 + 2.6 = 5.2X$

18. $1\frac{2}{5}Y = 4\frac{1}{6} - 2\frac{1}{3}$

19. Using algebraic symbols, represent: Three times a number, minus the number, plus twice the number, plus seven.

20. Write an equation and solve: What fraction of 4 is 3?

1. Sam borrowed four dollars to open a store. He made three dollars each day. Fill in the table on the right.

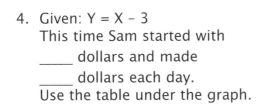

Day	Dollars
____	____
____	____
____	____
____	____

2. Plot these points and connect them.

3. Write an equation for the line.

(Dollars = ____ per day – ____ borrowed)

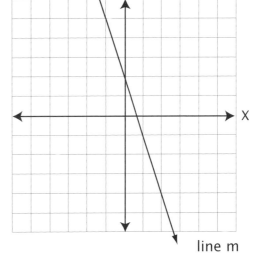

line m

4. Given: $Y = X - 3$
   This time Sam started with ____ dollars and made ____ dollars each day.
   Use the table under the graph.

5. Graph the points and the line.

6. The slope is ____ and the intercept is ____.

Day	Dollars
____	____
____	____
____	____
____	____

7. Estimate the slope and intercept of line *m* on the graph.

8. What would the equation of the line be using the slope–intercept formula?

9. This line is graphed within which quadrants?

10. Graph $X = -3$ and label it line *g*.

Simplify and solve for the unknown.

11. −9Q − 24Q + 15 = 0

12. 66 + 99A − 77 = 0

13. $2X(3 - 7 + 4 - 8 - 1) - 4^2 = (-4)$

14. 12 + 28 = −20B

15. 4D − .3D = 18.5

16. $6\frac{1}{2} = \frac{5}{7}N - 2\frac{3}{5}N$

17. −12 = −2A − 6

18. $-5\frac{1}{2}X + 2\frac{3}{8} = .9$

19. Using algebraic symbols, represent: The sum of a number plus one, times the sum of the number minus four.

20. Write an equation and solve: What fraction of 9 is 7?

Carpenters use the idea of slope when describing the steepness, or pitch, of a roof. The run is measured from the lowest part of the roof to a point under the highest point. The rise is the distance that the upper point is above the lowest point.

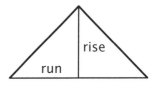

Graph a line representing the slope of each roof described below.

Let each space represent one foot and make the Y–intercept zero for each line. Notice the drawing shows mostly the first quadrant of the graph. The first one is done for you.

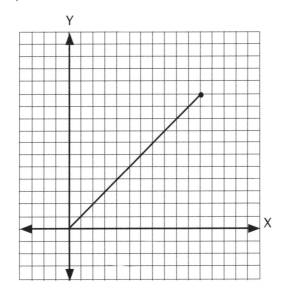

1. 11 ft run to 11 ft rise $\quad$ slope $= \dfrac{11}{11} = 1$

2. 12 ft run to 4 ft rise $\quad$ slope = _____

3. 15 ft run to 10 ft rise $\quad$ slope = _____

4. 6 ft run to 9 ft rise $\quad$ slope = _____

When computing "pitch," carpenters use the full width of the building instead of the run. If the roof is symmetrical, take two times the run to get the full width of the building.

Compute the pitch of each roof described below. The first one is done for you.

5. 12 ft run to 6 ft rise   pitch = $\dfrac{6}{24}$ = $\dfrac{1}{4}$ 2 x 12 is 24, so the width of the building is 24 feet. Use this number to find the pitch of the roof.

A carpenter might say that this roof was "quarter pitch."

6. 12 ft run to 8 ft rise   pitch = _____

7. 10 ft run to 10 ft rise   pitch = _____

8. 12 ft run to 18 ft rise   pitch = _____

Fill in the blanks.

1. Write the slope-intercept formula for lines *a*, *b*, *c*, and *d*.

    line *a*.   m = ___, b = ___,   Y = _____

    line *b*.   m = ___, b = ___,   Y = _____

    line *c*.   m = ___, b = ___,   Y = _____

    line *d*.   m = ___, b = ___,   Y = _____

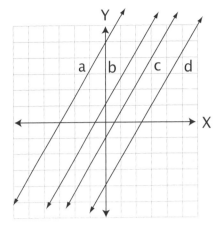

2. Write the slope-intercept formula for lines *w*, *x*, *y*, and *z*.

    line *w*.   m = ___, b = ___,   Y = _____

    line *x*.   m = ___, b = ___,   Y = _____

    line *y*.   m = ___, b = ___,   Y = _____

    line *z*.   m = ___, b = ___,   Y = _____

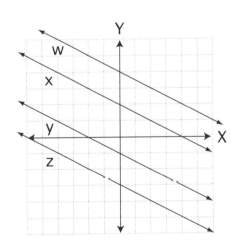

Be sure all the equations are in the slope–intercept form before comparing the slopes. There may be more than one answer for some of these questions.

3. Which of the following lines are parallel to $Y = -3X + 2$?

    A. $Y = 1/3\ X - 2$

    B. $Y = -3X$

    C. $Y = 4 - 3X$

4. Which of the following lines are parallel to $Y = 1/2\ X - 5$?

    A. $Y = 1/4\ X + 5$

    B. $Y = -1/2\ X + 2$

    C. $Y = 4 + 4/8\ X$

5. Which of the following lines are parallel to $2Y - 3X = 4$?

    A. $Y = 2/3\ X + 4$

    B. $Y = 6/4\ X$

    C. $2Y = 8 - 3X$

6. Which of the following lines are parallel to $3Y + 4X = -6$?

    A. $Y = 12/9\ X - 1$

    B. $3Y = -4X + 0$

    C. $-2Y = 5X - 8$

7. Change $-Y + 2X = 4$ to the slope-intercept form of the equation of a line.

8. Change $Y - 4X = 0$ to the slope-intercept form of the equation of a line.

9. Change $-2Y - X = -2$ to the slope-intercept form of the equation of a line.

10. Change $3Y - 2X = -6$ to the slope-intercept form of the equation of a line.

11. Change $-4Y - 3X = -8$ to the slope-intercept form of the equation of a line.

12. Change Y = -5/3 X - 2 to the standard form of the equation of a line.

13. Change Y = 4X - 3 to the standard form of the equation of a line.

14. Change Y = 1/4 X + 3 to the standard form of the equation of a line.

15. Change Y = -3/5 X - 1 to the standard form of the equation of a line.

16. Change Y = 3X to the standard form of the equation of a line.

Plot the points, draw a line to connect them, and find the slope–intercept formula for the line.

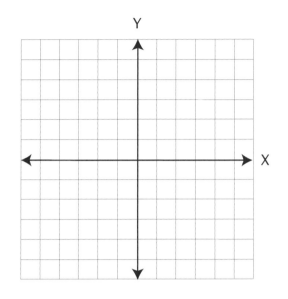
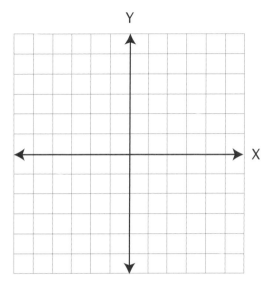

1. (–4, –6), (4, 0)

Y = _____

2. (–2, 2), (1, 5)

Y = _____

Plot the points and draw the line. Find the slope–intercept form and the standard form of the equation of the line.

3. (–3, –2), (4, –2)

Y = _____

_____

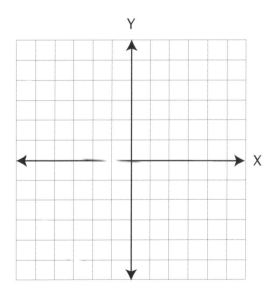

4. (0, 2), (6, –6)

Y = _____

_____

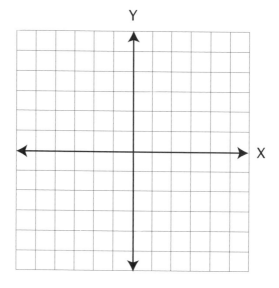

5. (–3, 6), (0, 0)

Y = _____

_____

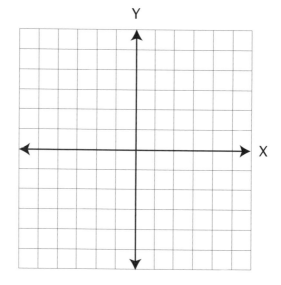

6. (3, 5), (3, –1)

Y = _____

_____

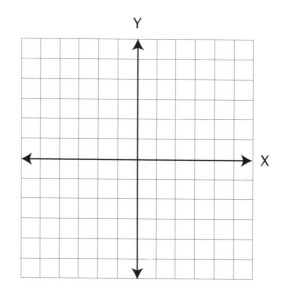

Follow the directions for each graph.

7. Plot the points (2, 0) and (4, –3).

8. Make a right triangle and determine the slope.

9. Estimate the intercept by extending the line until it intercepts the Y-axis.

10. Describe the new line using the slope-intercept formula.

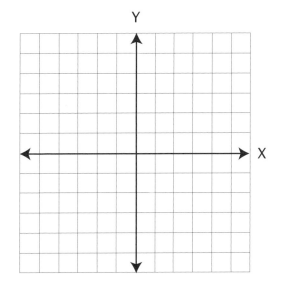

11. Which of the following lines are parallel to the line you drew? Put each equation into the slope-intercept form before answering.

    A.   2Y = 3X + 10

    B.   2Y – 3X = –4

    C.   2Y + 3X = 0

12. Draw a line that is parallel to the line described in #10, and that passes through the point (2, –5).

13. Describe the new line using the slope-intercept form of the equation of a line.

14. Describe the new line with the standard form of the equation of a line.

15. Plot the points (1, 3) and (–1, –5).

16. Make a right triangle and determine the slope.

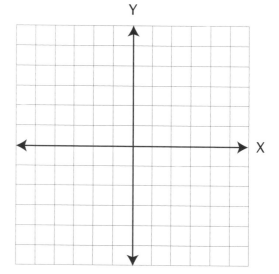

17. Estimate the intercept by extending the line until it intercepts the Y-axis.

18. Describe the new line using the slope-intercept formula.

19. Which of the following lines is parallel to Y = 3/2 X – 2?

    A.   2Y = –5X – 4

    B.   3Y = 6X

    C.   4Y = 6X + 4

20. Draw a line that is parallel to the line described in #18 that passes through the point (0, 3).

21. Describe the new line using the slope-intercept form of the equation of a line.

22. Describe the new line with the standard form of the equation of a line.

1. Plot the points (2, 6) and (–1, 3).

2. Make a right triangle and determine the slope.

3. Estimate the intercept by extending the line until it intercepts the Y-axis.

4. Describe the line using the slope-intercept form, and then give the standard form of the equation of a line.

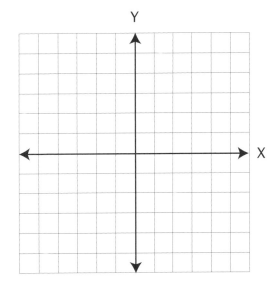

5. Which of the following lines is parallel to Y = –X + 2?

    A. 2Y = –2X – 2

    B. 3Y = 4X + 1

    C. 5Y = –5X

6. Draw a line that is parallel to the line described in #4 while passing through the point (2, 2).

7. What will be the slope of a line parallel to Y = 2X – 4?

8. What will be the slope of a line parallel to 4Y = –12X – 4?

9. Rewrite as the standard form of the equation of a line: Y – 3 = 1/3 X – 1.

10. Rewrite using the slope-intercept form: 2Y + 3X = 1.

Simplify and solve for the unknown.

11. $(3 - 11)^2 \times 2 \div 16 - 7 = 3Y - 4Y + 9$

12. $(3 - 5)^2 + | 6 - 4 | - X = 3X$

13. $3(A - 4) - 5(2A - 6) = 21$

14. $1\frac{1}{3} + \frac{4}{5} A = 2\frac{1}{5}$

Simplify.

15. $-6^2 - (-6)^2 =$

16. $5 + 5 - (-7) =$

17. $-[-(-7)] =$

18. $(-8)^2 =$

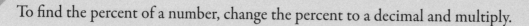

QUICK REVIEW

To find the percent of a number, change the percent to a decimal and multiply.

EXAMPLE   Shipping is 8%. What will it cost to ship a package worth $25.50?

8% is the same as .08.

25.50 x .08 = $2.04 cost of shipping

19. Mr. Brown gets a profit of 25% of the total (retail) cost of each item he sells. What is his profit on an item that sells for $76.98? Round your answer to the nearest hundredth.

20. Forty-five percent of the people had brown eyes. If there were 600 people, how many had brown eyes?

1. Plot the points (5, 1) and (−1, −5).

2. Make a right triangle and determine the slope.

3. Estimate the intercept by extending the line until it intercepts the Y-axis.

4. Describe the line using the slope-intercept form, and then give the standard form of the equation of a line.

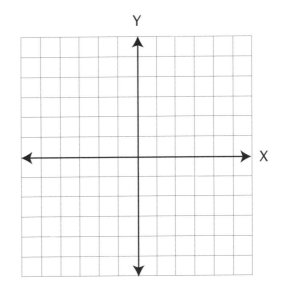

5. Which of the following lines is parallel to Y = 1/4 X − 3?

    A. 2Y = 1/3 X + 2

    B. 4Y = 4X + 3

    C. 3Y = 3/4 X + 6

6. Draw a line that is parallel to Y = 1/4 X − 3 while passing through the point (0, −1).

7. Describe the new line using the slope-intercept form.

8. What will be the slope of a line parallel to 3Y = −6X + 9?

9. Rewrite in the standard form of the equation of a line: Y = 2X + 5.

10. Rewrite using the slope-intercept form: 4Y + 2X = 8.

Simplify and solve for the unknown.

11. $|-1 - 1 - 1 - 1|^2 = (-1)^2 + B(-1) \div 1$

12. $(3 + 5)^2 + |8 - 11| + Z = 4(Z - 2)$

13. $5(B - 6) + 4(2B + 7) = 102$ 14. $55Q - 30Q = 125$

Simplify.

15. $-\{-[-(-8)]\}$ 16. $-9^2 =$

17. $-(-4) =$ 18. $3^2 + (-3)^2 =$

19. A Canadian came to America and exchanged his money for U.S. dollars at an exchange rate of 76%. If he exchanged $200, how much did he receive in U.S. funds? (Find 76% of 200.)

20. WF x 8 = 2 (Check your answer by multiplying.)

1. Plot the points (–1, –1) and (–3, 3).

2. Make a right triangle and determine the slope.

3. Estimate the intercept by extending the line until it intercepts the Y-axis.

4. Describe the line using the slope-intercept form, and then give the standard form.

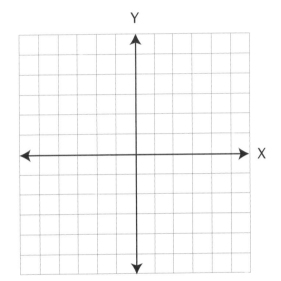

5. Which of the following lines is parallel to Y = 3X + 1?

    A. 4Y = –4X – 4

    B. 1/2 Y = 3/2 X

    C. Y = 3X – 2

6. Draw a line that is parallel to the line given in #5 while passing through the point (1, 1).

7. Describe the new line using the slope-intercept form.

8. What will be the slope of a line parallel to Y = –1/5 X?

9. Rewrite in the standard form: Y = –3X – 6.

10. Rewrite in the slope-intercept form: 5Y + 10X = –5.

Simplify and solve for the unknown.

11. $24Y - 108Y + 96 = 48 - 12Y$

12. $\{ -[-(-9)] + 7^2\} \div 5 \div 2 = Q + 4$

13. $8(A + 3 - 9) - 4(2A + 5) = 2A + 4$

14. $(6 + 6)^2 + |\ 100 - 1\ | - 14^2 = 5 \times 9 + B$

Simplify.

15. $-[-(6 - 9 + 3 - 5)] =$

16. $-5^3 =$

Answer the questions.

17. WF x 10 = 3   (Check your answer by multiplying.)

18. Joseph spent $8.75 for baseball cards at $.25 per pack. How many packs did he buy?

19. The tax on sales is 6%. How much tax is owed on a purchase of $115?

20. Rewrite using algebraic symbols: the opposite of a number squared, minus a number squared.

Equations used to solve word problems can be divided into segments.
Consider the following example:

The cost of white copy paper is $3.00 a ream for the first 10 reams. If you order between 11 and 19 reams, the cost drops to $2.75 per ream. If you buy 20 or more reams, the cost is $2.50 per ream. (A ream of paper is 500 sheets.)

You can express this problem in the following way:

(C stands for cost, and X is a positive integer representing the number of reams.)

$$C = 3.00X \text{ if } 0 \leq X \leq 10 \quad C = 2.75X \text{ if } 11 \leq X < 20 \quad C = 2.50X \text{ if } X \geq 20$$

Example What would the cost be for 15 reams of paper?
15 is between 11 and 20, so 15 x 2.75 = $41.25.

Answer the questions.

1. What would the cost be for 12 reams of paper?

2. What would the cost be for five reams of paper?

3. If you have only $50 to spend on copy paper, how many reams can you purchase? First find the cost of the most reams that can be bought at the highest cost and the fewest reams that can be bought at the lowest cost. You will then know which cost category and which equation you must use.

A furniture store charges interest on credit card purchases. If the balance exceeds $1,000, the service charge is 0.8% per month. If the balance is $1,000 or less, the finance charge is 1.2% per month. On balances under $50, there is a $1 service charge per month. $0 balances do not incur any charge.

4. Write four equations to compute the monthly service charge (C) on a customer's balance (B).

5. What would be the service charge on an outstanding balance of $600?

6. If a $7 service charge was incurred, how much was the balance on the account?

A worker receives $10 an hour for every hour he works, up through 40 hours a week. He receives $15 an hour for each hour over 40 (overtime) that he works each week. This is called time and a half, since he gets 1 1/2 times $10, or $15. If he is required to work on a holiday, he receives $20 an hour for each hour worked. $20 is double his salary of $10 and so is referred to as double time.

7. Write three equations to compute the pay (P) per hours worked (H).

8. What should the worker described above receive for 40 hours work?

9. During one week, he worked 40 regular hours, five overtime hours and six holiday hours. What was his total pay?

10. Last week the worker received $580 in his paycheck. How many hours had he worked if no holidays were involved?

Follow the directions for each graph.

1. Plot the points (1, 4) and (–1, –4).

2. Make a right triangle and
   determine the slope.

3. Extend the line and estimate
   the Y–intercept.

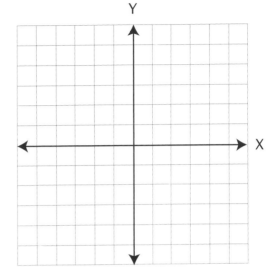

4. Describe the line with the
   slope–intercept form.

5. Which of the following lines is perpendicular to the line you drew?

   A.   Y = 4X + 2

   B.   Y = –1/4 X

   C.   Y = –4X – 2

6. Draw a line that is perpendicular to the original line while passing
   through the point (0, 2).

7. Describe the new line with the slope–intercept form.

8. Describe the new line using the standard form of the equation of a line.

9. Plot the points (–3, 1) and (–1, –1).

10. Make a right triangle and determine the slope.

11. Extend the line and estimate the Y–intercept.

12. Describe the line with the slope-intercept form.

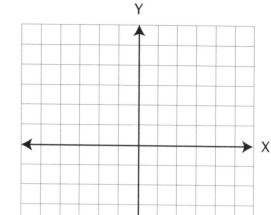

13. Which of the following lines is perpendicular to the line you drew?

    A. 2Y = 2X – 4

    B. Y = 4X + 2

    C. Y = –1/2 X + 2

14. Draw a line that is perpendicular to the original line, while passing through the point (2, 4).

15. Describe the new line with the slope-intercept form.

16. Describe the new line using the standard form of the equation of a line.

Follow the directions for each graph.

1. Plot the points (–4, 3) and (4, 1).

2. Make a right triangle and determine the slope.

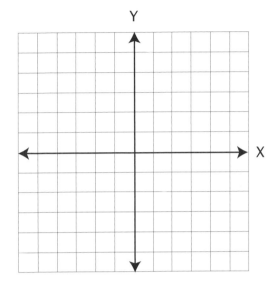

3. Extend the line and estimate the Y–intercept.

4. Describe the line with the slope-intercept form.

5. Which of the following lines is perpendicular to the line you drew?

    A.   2Y = 8X – 10

    B.   Y = –1/4 X – 2

    C.   4Y = –X + 8

6. Draw a line that is perpendicular to the original line while passing through the point (–2, –4).

7. Describe the new line with the slope-intercept form.

8. Describe the new line using the standard form of the equation of a line.

9. Plot the points (2, 3) and (–2, –1).

10. Make a right triangle and determine the slope.

11. Extend the line and estimate the Y–intercept.

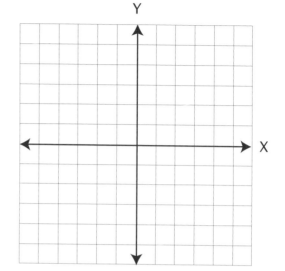

12. Describe the line with the slope–intercept form.

13. Which of the following lines is perpendicular to the line you drew?

    A. $Y = -X + 1$

    B. $Y = 1/2 \, X - 1$

    C. $Y = -1/2 \, X + 2$

14. Draw a line that is perpendicular to the original line while passing through the point (1, –5).

15. Describe the new line with the slope–intercept form.

16. Describe the new line using the standard form of the equation of a line.

1. Plot the points (–3, –5) and (3, –3).

2. Make a right triangle and determine the slope.

3. Estimate the intercept by extending the line until it intercepts the Y-axis.

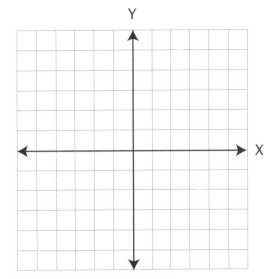

4. Describe the line using the slope–intercept form, and then give in the standard form of the equation of a line.

5. Which of the following lines is perpendicular to the line in #4?

   A. Y = – 1/3 X + 3

   B. Y = –3X – 1

   C. 4Y = –12X – 4

6. Draw a line that is perpendicular to the line given in #4 while passing through the point (3, –3).

7. Describe the perpendicular line with the slope–intercept form, and then with the standard form of the equation.

8. Draw a line that is perpendicular to the line given in #4 while passing through the point (0, –4).

9. Describe the new line with the slope–intercept form, then with the standard form of the equation of a line.

10. What do you notice about the slopes of the lines you drew for #6 and #8?

Simplify and solve for the unknown.

11. 6X − X + 3 = 4X + 7

12. −2X − X + 12 = X − 12

13. |−(3 + 7)| − 4^2 + $(−4)^2$ = 2R

14. $-3\dfrac{1}{2}$ Y + $\dfrac{2}{9}$ = $-\dfrac{4}{3}$

15. 60% of the shoe store's receipts go towards paying for the shoes (cost of goods sold). What percent of the receipts is profit? (Hint: Remember that cost plus profit equals 100%.)

16. If the first-quarter sales totaled $12,900, what is the amount of profit?

17. Self-employment tax is 15.3% of the profit. How much do you, the proprietor, have to pay?

18. If two bits is worth 25¢, how much is one bit worth?

19. How much is eight bits worth?

20. At the beginning of the year, Devan had $3.00. Each week thereafter, his uncle gave him $5.00. Write an equation showing how his money increased.

1. Plot the points (2, –3) and (–1, 3).

2. Make a right triangle and determine the slope.

3. Estimate the intercept by extending the line until it intercepts the Y-axis.

4. Describe the line with the slope-intercept form, and then give in the standard form.

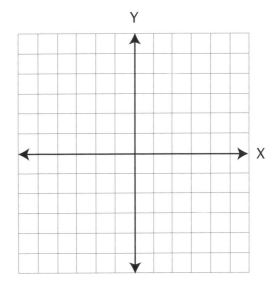

5. Which of the following lines is perpendicular to the line in #4?

   A. Y = 1/2 X – 1

   B. Y = 5/2 X + 2

   C. 3Y = 6X – 3

6. Draw a line that is perpendicular to the line given in #4 while passing through the point (4, 1).

7. Describe the perpendicular line with the slope-intercept form, and then with the standard form of the equation.

8. Draw a line perpendicular to the line given in #4 passing through the point (2, 4).

9. Describe the new line with the slope-intercept form, and then with the standard form of the equation of a line.

10. What do you notice about the slopes of the lines you drew for #6 and #8?

Simplify and solve for the unknown.

11. $2X + 2 - X + 2X = 3X - 3 + 10 - X$

12. $3Y - 1 + 2Y - 1 - 4Y = 2Y + 3 + Y + 1$

13. $-(6 + 7)^2 + (10 + 5)^2 = 5M$

14. $-1\frac{2}{3} = -2\frac{1}{4} + 1\frac{1}{5}A$

15. 55% of the shoe store's receipts go towards paying for the shoes (cost of goods sold). What percent of the receipts is profit?

16. If the second-quarter sales totaled $9,645, what is the amount of profit?

17. Self-employment tax is 15.3% of the profit. How much do you, the proprietor, have to pay?

18. If two bits is worth 25¢, how many bits are in $2.50?

19. How much is 100 bits worth?

20. At the beginning of the month, the vine measured five feet. Thereafter, it grew one foot per week. Write an equation describing the growth of the vine.

1. Plot the points (–2, 1) and (–3, 2).

2. Make a right triangle and determine the slope.

3. Estimate the intercept by extending the line until it intercepts the Y-axis.

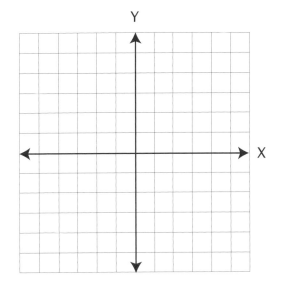

4. Describe the line with the slope-intercept form, and then give in the standard form of the equation of a line.

5. Which of the following lines is perpendicular to the line in #4?

    A.   Y = 5X – 5
    B.   Y = 1/2 X
    C.   Y = X – 2

6. Draw a line that is perpendicular to the line given in #4 while passing through the point (3, 1).

7. Describe the perpendicular line you drew in #6 with the slope-intercept form, then with the standard form of the equation of a line.

Simplify and solve for the unknown.

8. $5Y - 3 - 2Y + 4 + 3Y = 4Y + 9 + 4Y$

9. $-M - 4 - 2M + 20 = M + 7 - 5M + 11$

10. $|-3 - 4 - 5 + 2| + W = 3W$

11. $3\frac{1}{4}B = 3\frac{2}{9} + \frac{5}{12}$

12. 48% of the shoe store's receipts go towards paying for the shoes (cost of goods sold). What percent of the receipts is profit?

13. If the third-quarter sales totaled $25,813, what is the amount of profit?

14. Self-employment tax is 15.3% of the profit. How much do you, the proprietor, have to pay?

15. If one pound is 20 shillings, and one shilling is 12 pence, how many pence are in one pound?

16. Five pounds = _____ shillings

17. Katie started her business with $1,000. Unfortunately the business lost $20 a week after that. Write an equation showing the condition of Katie's business.

QUICK REVIEW

The radical, or square root sign, indicates the factor which may be multiplied times itself to yield the given number.

EXAMPLE $\sqrt{16} = 4$ because 4 x 4 = 16

Find the square root.

18. $\sqrt{100} =$ 19. $\sqrt{36} =$ 20. $\sqrt{144} =$

10H

Not all information plotted on a graph with X and Y coordinates forms a straight line. A graph made with information that lacks a noticeable pattern can be called a "scatter diagram."

Follow the directions.

1. Universities are interested in studying the relationship between students' incoming test scores and their freshman grade-point averages. Plot the points on the graph. Note that even though all the lines have not been completely drawn, this is the first quadrant of a Cartesian coordinate system.

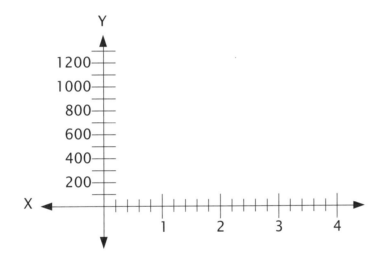

freshman GPA (X)	test score (Y)
3.4	1300
3.2	1200
3.2	1100
3.0	1100
2.8	1000
2.5	800

2. A group of high school students took the same college-entrance test two times. The data below shows the changes in scores from the first to the second testing. It also shows the number of students that had each change in score. Plot the points on the graph.

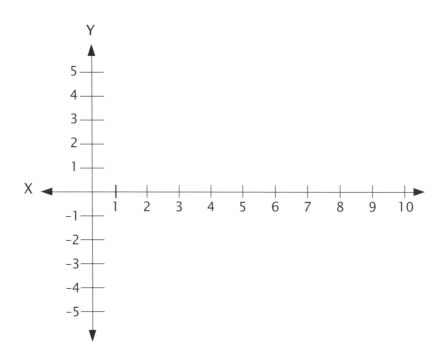

# of students (X)	change in score (Y)
1	−5
2	−4
3	−3
6	−2
8	−1
10	0
7	1
5	2
4	3

Follow the directions.

1. Draw a line with m = 3 through the point (1, 2).

2. Estimate the Y-intercept.

3. Describe the line using the slope-intercept form.

4. Now describe the line using the standard form of the equation of a line.

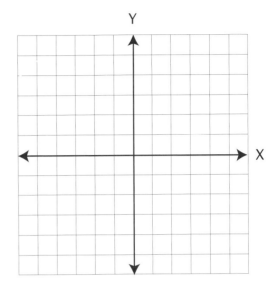

5. Find the slope of the line passing through the points (–2, 1) and (6, 3), then draw to check.

6. Find the intercept by computing first. Then confirm by checking your drawing from #5.

7. Describe the line using the slope-intercept form.

8. Now describe the line using the standard form of the equation of a line.

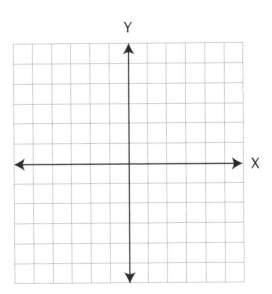

Given the slope of the line and a point on the line, describe the following lines using the slope–intercept form.

9. m = 5; (1, 2)

10. m = 6; (-3, 6)

11. m = -4; (1, 1)

12. m = 1/2; (2, 2)

13. m = 2/3; (5, 8)

14. m = -1/4; (2, 1)

Given two points on a line, find the slope and Y–intercept of the line, and then describe it using the slope–intercept form.

15. (2, 3) (4, 5)

16. (4, 6) (2, 1)

17. (3, 3) (1, 0)

Follow the directions.

1. Draw a line with m = 1/2 through the point (3, 2).

2. Estimate the Y-intercept, and then check by computing.

3. Describe the line using the slope-intercept form.

4. Now describe the line using the standard equation of a line.

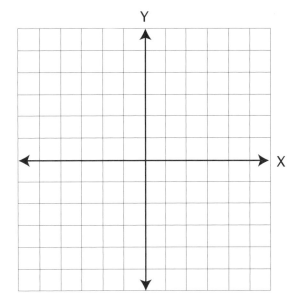

5. Find the slope of the lines passing through the points (-4, 5) and (2, -2), and then draw to check.

6. Find the intercept by computing first. Then confirm by checking your drawing from #5.

7. Describe the line using the slope-intercept form.

8. Now describe the line using the standard equation of a line.

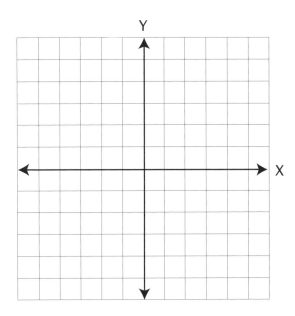

Given the slope of the line and a point on the line, describe the following lines using the slope–intercept form.

9. m = 8; (1, 2)

10. m = 3; (1, 2)

11. m = -2; (3, 0)

Given two points on a line, find the slope and Y-intercept of the line, and then describe it using the slope-intercept form.

12. (2, 5) (-2, 3)

13. (5, 2) (1, 1)

14. (-2, -3) (-3, 1)

15. (-5, -6) (-2, -1)

16. (5, -3) (-1, 6)

17. (7, 2) (-3, 8)

SYSTEMATIC REVIEW

11C

Follow the directions.

1. Draw the line: m = 1/4
   through the point (-5, 1).

2. Find the intercept (b).

3. Describe using the slope–intercept
   form, then using the standard form
   of the equation of a line.

4. Find the slope through (1, 2) and
   (-3, 2) by computing, and then
   drawing to check.

5. Find the intercept both ways
   (computing and drawing).

6. Describe using the slope–intercept
   form, then using the standard
   form of the equation of a line.

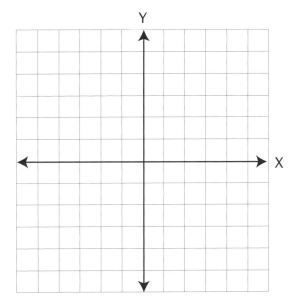

7. Draw a line parallel to Y = -2X - 1,
   through (-1, 5).

8. Describe using the slope–intercept
   form, then using the standard
   form of the equation of a line.

9. Draw a line perpendicular to
   Y = 3X - 2, through (3, 1).

10. Describe using the slope–intercept
    form, then using the standard form
    of the equation of a line.

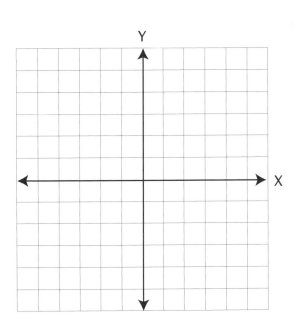

Tell if each of the following is an example of the associative, commutative, or distributive property.

11. $3(4X - 2) = 12X - 6$ 12. $(-3)(-16) = (-16)(-3)$

13. $2A + 2B = 2B + 2A$ 14. $(X + Y) + Z = X + (Y + Z)$

Solve.

15. $\sqrt{9} =$ 16.   45% of 98 =

QUICK REVIEW

A ratio may be written as a fraction and then changed to a percent.

EXAMPLE 1   The ratio of blondes to brunettes in the class is 2 to 3. What is the ratio of blondes to the total number of people?

$\dfrac{2 \text{ Blondes}}{5 \text{ Total}} = \dfrac{2}{5}$

EXAMPLE 2   What percent of the class is blonde?

$\dfrac{2}{5} = 2 \div 5 = .40 = 40\%$

EXAMPLE 3   If there are 20 students in the class, how many are blonde? $.4 \times 20 = 8$ blondes

17.   In our family there are five boys and one girl. What is the ratio of boys to girls?

18.   What is the ratio of boys to the total?

19.   What percent of the family is boys? (Round to hundredths.)

20.   If the extended family has 48 children with the same ratio of boys to girls, how many are boys? Use your fractional answer to #18 to compute, rather than using the rounded percent, or you will get part of a boy!

Follow the directions.

1. Draw the line given: m = -2/5 through the point (1, 1).

2. Find the intercept (b).

3. Describe using the slope-intercept form, then using the standard form of the equation of a line.

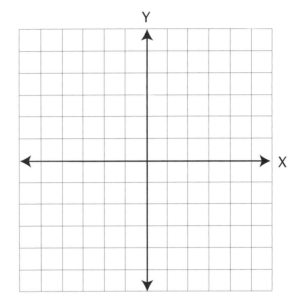

4. Find the slope through (-1, 4) and (3, 2) by computing, and then drawing to check.

5. Find the intercept both ways (computing and drawing).

6. Describe using the slope-intercept form, then using the standard form of the equation of a line.

7. Draw a line parallel to Y = -1/3 X - 4, through (3, -3).

8. Describe using the slope-intercept form, then using the standard form of the equation of a line.

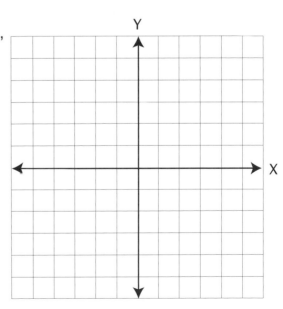

9. Draw a line perpendicular to Y = 2/3 X - 2, through (2, 1).

10. Describe using the slope-intercept form, then using the standard form of the equation of a line.

True or false.

11. Addition is associative.

12. Subtraction is associative.

13. Division is commutative.

14. Multiplication is commutative.

Solve.

15. $\sqrt{49} =$

16. 16% of 32 =

17. In our community you are either a Steelers or an Eagles fan. The ratio of Steelers fans to Eagles fans is 5 to 3. What is the ratio of Steelers fans to total fans? What percent is this?

18. What is the ratio of Eagles fans to total fans? What percent is this?

19. If there are 640 fans, how many are Eagles fans and how many are Steelers fans?

20. The growth in Sam's savings account is expressed by the equation Y = 20X + 100, where X is the number of weeks he has been saving, and Y is the total amount of money in the account. If he has been saving for 15 weeks at this rate, what is his total savings?

Follow the directions.

1. Draw the line given: m = -1 through the point (4, -1).

2. Find the intercept (b).

3. Describe using the slope-intercept form, and then using the standard form of the equation of a line.

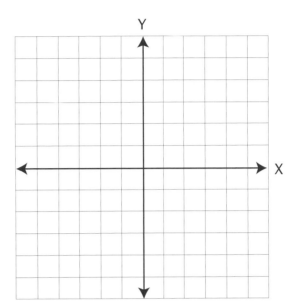

4. Find the slope through (1, 2) and (-4, 5) by computing, then drawing to check.

5. Find the intercept both ways (computing and drawing).

6. Describe using the slope-intercept form, then using the standard form of the equation of a line.

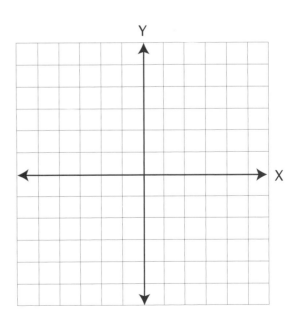

7. Draw a line parallel to Y = -X - 2, through (-2, 3).

8. Describe using the slope-intercept form, then using the standard form of the equation of a line.

9. Draw a line perpendicular to Y = 4X + 1, through (-1, 3).

10. Describe using the slope-intercept form, then using the standard form of the equation of a line.

Solve for the unknown.

11. $(-1)(2)(-3)(4)(-5)^2 = -\{-[-(-X)]\}$

12. $72A - 84A = 36AF \ (A \neq 0)$

13. $-4.2Q - 1.8Q = -6$

14. $.14 - .023 = .07C$

Answer the questions

15. The ratio of flour to water in the paste is 3 to 2. What is the ratio of water to paste? What percent is this?

16. What is the ratio of flour to the total amount of paste? What percent is this?

17. There are 500 grams of paste. How many grams of water are there?

18. How many grams of flour are there?

QUICK TIP

If you are not comfortable with measurement equivalents, this is a good time to learn them. Check the "Symbols and Tables" page in the back of this book for help.

19. Since there are 5,280 feet in one mile, how many feet are there in 4 1/2 miles?

20. How many yards are there in one mile?

Many kinds of word problems can be solved by using equations that describe a line.

Read each word problem and answer the questions.

Sam received a starting bonus of $50 when he signed up for his new job. After that, he received a daily wage. At the end of five days, Sam had gained a total of $400 from his job. At the end of 10 days, his gain was $750. Follow the steps to write an equation, or formula, that you can use to find the amount of money Sam will have gained after any given number of days.

1. Plot the points (0, 50) and (5, 400) on the graph and connect them. Make each space on the Y-axis worth $25 and each space on the X-axis worth five days. Note that when making a graph like this, you may choose any scale that is convenient for the problem, but you should always record what scale is being used.

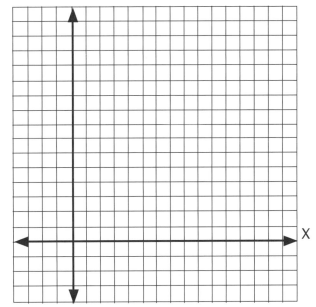

2. Use the points given above to find the slope of the line.

3. Use the slope and one set of points to find the value of b, and write an equation in the form Y = mX + b.

4. Rewrite your equation using G (gain) instead of Y and T (number of days) instead of X.

5. Use your equation to find Sam's gain after 30 days.

The percentage of spinach seeds that will germinate (start to grow) depends on temperature in a linear way.

At 10°C, 50% of the seeds will germinate, and at 15°C, 80% will germinate.

6. Following the same steps as above, write a linear equation where Y is replaced by G for the percentage of germinated seeds and X is replaced with T for temperature.

7. Use your equation to find the percentage of spinach seeds that should germinate if the temperature is 12°C.

8. At what temperature will 90% of the seeds germinate?

Follow the steps to graph each inequality.

For #1-4 $3Y \leq X + 9$

1. Graph $3Y = X + 9$. (Hint: First change to slope–intercept form.)

2. Will this be a solid line or a dotted line?

3. Choose two points, one on each side of the line. (___ , ___) (___ , ___)

4. Shade in the graph.

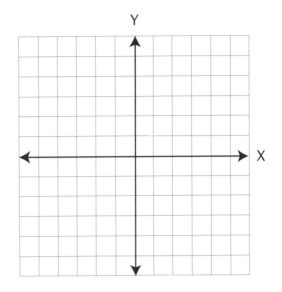

For #5-8 $2Y > -X - 4$

5. Graph $2Y = -X - 4$.

6. Will this be a solid line or a dotted line?

7. Choose two points, one on each side of the line. (___ , ___) (___ , ___)

8. Shade in the graph.

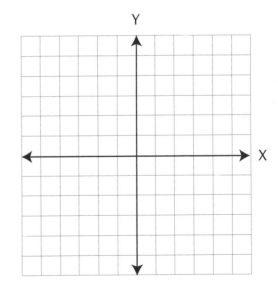

For #9-12 $-3X - Y \leq -1$

(Hint: Multiplying or dividing by a negative number always changes the direction of an inequality.)

9. Graph $3X + Y = 1$.

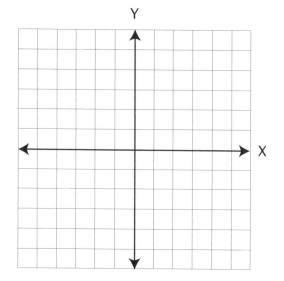

10. Will this be a solid line or a dotted line?

11. Choose two points, one on each side of the line.
    (___ , ___) (___ , ___)

12. Shade in the graph.

Write each inequality in the slope–intercept form.

13. $X + Y > -2$

14. $-2Y + 4X < 6$

15. $-4Y - 8X \geq 8$

Follow the steps to graph each inequality.

For #1–4 $-2X + Y \leq -3$

1. Graph $-2X + Y = -3$.

2. Will this be a solid line or a dotted line?

3. Choose two points, one on each side of the line.
   (___ , ___) (___ , ___)

4. Shade in the graph.

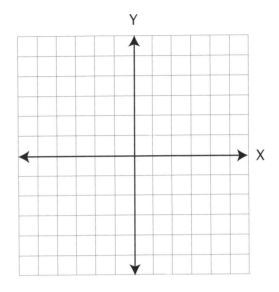

For #5–8 $3Y \leq 2X - 9$

5. Graph $3Y = 2X - 9$.

6. Will this be a solid line or a dotted line?

7. Choose two points, one on each side of the line.
   (___ , ___) (___ , ___)

8. Shade in the graph.

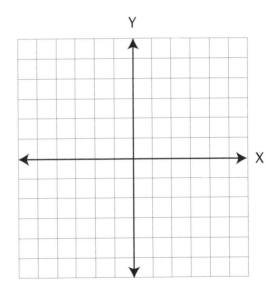

For #9-12   –X + 5Y > 5

9. Graph –X + 5Y = 5.

10. Will this be a solid line or a dotted line?

11. Choose two points, one on each side of the line.
(___ , ___) (___ , ___)

12. Shade in the graph.

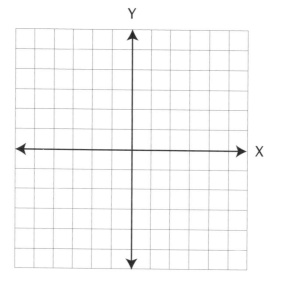

Write each inequality in the slope–intercept form.

13. –3X + Y < –5

14. 3X – Y > 5

15. For what operations should the sign of an inequality be reversed?

Follow the steps to graph each inequality.

For #1–5   –Y > –2X – 1

1. Graph Y = 2X + 1.

2. Will this be a solid line or a dotted line?

3. Choose two points, one on each side of the line.
   (___ , ___) (___ , ___)

4. Shade in the graph.

5. Is the point (3, –2) a solution of the inequality?

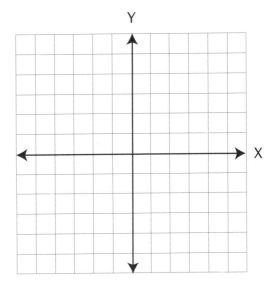

For #6–10   Y ≤ X – 3

6. Graph Y = X – 3.

7. Will this be a solid line or a dotted line?

8. Choose two points, one on each side of the line.
   (___ , ___) (___ , ___)

9. Shade in the graph.

10. For what operations must the sign of an inequality be reversed?

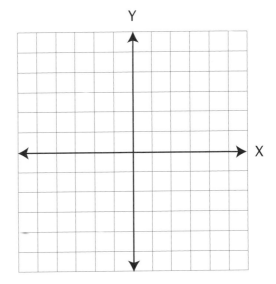

Answer the questions.

11. What fraction of a pound is an ounce?

12. What fraction of a ton is a pound?

13. Change to the slope-intercept form: 3X – 2Y = 5.

14. What is the slope of a line parallel to the line in #13?

15. What is the slope of a line perpendicular to the line in #13?

16. Write the equation for a line with a slope of 2 that passes through the point (0, –2).

17. 16% of 242 =

18. The point (–2, –2) lies in which quadrant?

QUICK REVIEW

Ratios are useful in solving some kinds of measurement problems.

EXAMPLE 1   Since 1 mile = 1.6 km, 5 miles = _____ km. $\frac{1}{1.6} = \frac{5}{?}$
Using cross-multiplication
(1)(?) = (1.6)(5) → ? = 8, so answer is 8 km.

EXAMPLE 2   Since 1 mile = 1.6 km, _____ miles = 1 km. $\frac{1}{1.6} = \frac{?}{1}$
Using cross-multiplication
(1)(1) = (1.6)(?) → 1 ÷ 1.6 = ?, so answer is .625 km.

19.   Since 1 mile = 1.6 km, 10 miles = _____ km.

20.   Since 1 mile = 1.6 km, _____ miles = 10 km.

Follow the steps to graph each inequality.

For #1-5   Y + 2 < 0

1. Graph Y + 2 = 0.

2. Will this be a solid line or a dotted line?

3. Choose two points, one on each side of the line.
   (___, ___) (___, ___)

4. Shade in the graph.

5. Write 4Y + 8 < 0 in slope-intercept form.

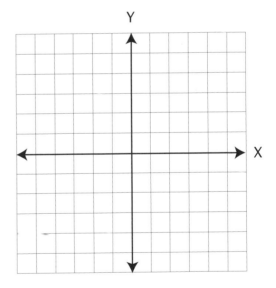

For #6-10   Y – 3 > 1/3 X – 1

6. Graph Y – 3 = 1/3 X – 1.

7. Will this be a solid line or a dotted line?

8. Choose two points, one on each side of the line.
   (___, ___) (___, ___)

9. Shade in the graph.

10. Write –3Y > –6X + 3 in slope-intercept form.

Answer the questions.

11. What fraction of an hour is a minute?

12. What percent of a week is a day?

13. Since 1 pound = .45 kg, 10 lb = ____ kg.

14. Since 1 pound = .45 kg, ____ lb = 2 kg.

15. What is the slope of a line parallel to 6Y – 4X –3 = 0?

16. What is the slope of a line perpendicular to the line in #15?

17. Write the equation for a line with a slope of –1/2 that passes through the point (1,1).

18. Change 9/25 to a decimal and to a percent.

19. Write in algebraic terms: six times a number, minus five times the number, plus eight.

20. Replace the number in #19 with 10 and find the value of the expression.

Follow the steps to graph each inequality.

For #1–5 $Y \leq 2X + 3$

1. Graph $Y = 2X + 3$.

2. Will this be a solid line or a
    dotted line?

3. Choose two points, one on
    each side of the line.
    (___, ___) (___, ___)

4. Shade in the graph.

5. Is the point (3, 1) a solution of
    the inequality?

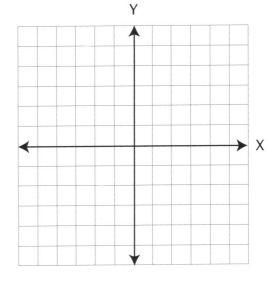

For #6–10 $-X \leq -4$

6. Graph $X = 4$.

7. Will this be a solid line or a
    dotted line?

8. Choose two points, one on
    each side of the line.
    (___, ___) (___, ___)

9. Shade in the graph.

10. For what operations must the
    sign of an inequality be reversed?

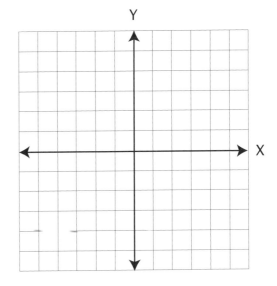

Answer the questions.

11. What fraction of a gallon is a pint?

12. What percent of a gallon is a quart?

13. Since 1 quart = .95 liters, 1 gallon = _____ liters.

14. Since 1 quart = .95 liters, _____ quarts = 1 liter.

15. What is the slope of a line parallel to 1/2 Y = X + 16?

16. What is the slope of a line perpendicular to the line in #15?

17. Write the equation for a line with a slope of 3 that passes through the point (–3, –4).

18. Change 12/17 to a decimal (round to hundredths) and to a percent.

19. 17% of 425 =

20. The point (5, –5) lies in which quadrant?

Here are some more word problems that use linear equations.

Read each word problem, and answer the questions.

Speedy Car Rental has two plans for renting its vehicles. Either you can pay $20 per day *and* $.15 per mile, or you can pay a flat fee of $30 per day.

1. Write an equation for the one day cost of the first plan in terms of cost (C) and number of miles (M).

2. Write an equation for the one day cost of the second plan in terms of cost (C) and number of miles (M).

3. If you are planning to rent a car for two days and drive for 80 miles, which plan will be cheaper?

A ramp for a wheelchair access has a slope of 5%. (Five feet vertically for every 100 feet horizontally.) The entire ramp is built on level ground. The entrance to the house is two feet above the ground. The horizontal distance in feet between the ends of the ramp needs to be found.

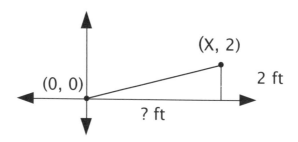

4.   Write the slope of the line (ramp) in fraction form.

5.   You know the slope, the Y-coordinates for two points, and the X-coordinate for one point. Using the formula for finding slope when two points are known, solve for X, which is the desired distance.

Follow the directions for each graph.

1. Draw line *a*: Y = 1/2 X + 3/2.

   For problems where a point is an improper fraction, it is easier to convert to a mixed number. Place the point as accurately as you can: it doesn't need to be exact.

2. Draw line *b*: Y = –1/2 X + 5/2.

3. What is the point where line *a* and line *b* intersect?

4. Draw line *c*: Y = –2X + 2.

5. Draw line *d*: Y = 1/3 X – 5.

6. What is the point where line *c* and line *d* intersect?

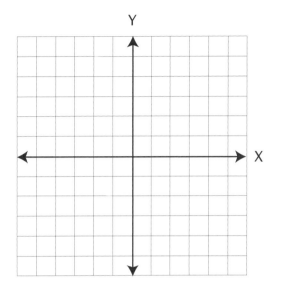

7. Draw line *e*: Y = –2X – 4.

8. Draw line *f*: Y = 1/3 X + 3.

9. What is the point where line *e* and line *f* intersect?

10. Draw line *g*: Y = –1/3 X + 2.

11. Draw line *h*: Y = 2X – 5.

12. What is the point where line *g* and line *h* intersect?

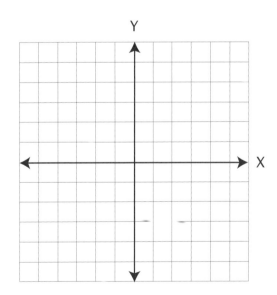

13. Draw line *j*: Y = 3X – 2.

14. Draw line *k*: Y = –2X + 3.

15. What is the point where line *j* and line *k* intersect?

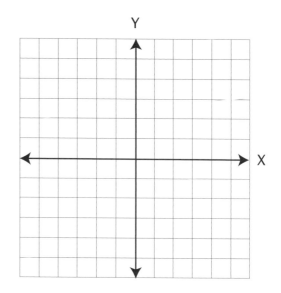

16. Draw line *r*: Y = 7X + 4.

17. Draw line *s*: Y = –3X – 6.

18. What is the point where line *r* and line *s* intersect?

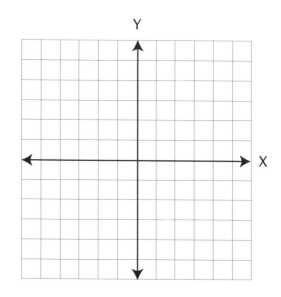

Follow the directions for each graph.

1. Draw line *a*: Y = 2X + 5/2.

2. Draw line *b*: Y = –1/2 X + 5/2.

3. What is the point where line *a* and line *b* intersect?

4. Draw line *c*: Y = –1/2 X – 2.

5. Draw line *d*: Y = –X – 3.

6. What is the point where line *c* and line *d* intersect?

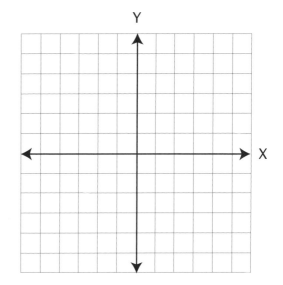

7. Draw line *e*: X – Y = 2.

8. Draw line *f*: X + 3Y = 6.

9. What is the point where line *e* and line *f* intersect?

10. Draw line *g*: 2X + Y = –2.

11. Draw line *h*: Y = 1/3 X + 5.

12. What is the point where line *g* and line *h* intersect?

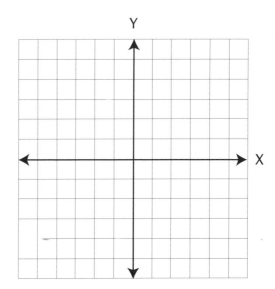

13. Draw line *j*: 4Y = –X + 12.

14. Draw line *k*: Y = X + 3.

15. What is the point where line *j* and line *k* intersect?

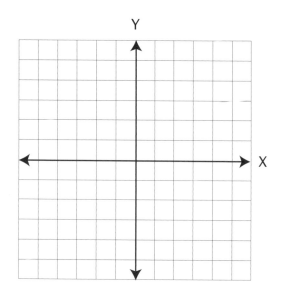

16. Draw line *r*: 2Y = –X – 2.

17. Draw line *s*: Y = 1/2 X – 3.

18. What is the point where line *r* and line *s* intersect?

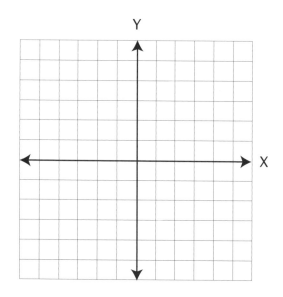

Follow the directions.

1. Draw line *a*: Y = –4X – 2.
   Label it *a*.

2. Draw line *b*: Y = X + 3.
   Label it *b*.

3. Record the point where line *a*
   and line *b* intersect.

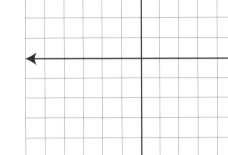

4. **Given:** m = –4 through the
   point (1, –3).

   Find the intercept (b).

5. Describe the line in #4 using the
   slope–intercept form, then using
   the standard equation of a line.

6. Find the slope through (5,1) and (–5, –5) by computing. $\dfrac{Y_2 - Y_1}{X_2 - X_1} = m$

7. Find the intercept of the line in #6.

8. Describe the line in #6 using the slope–intercept form, then using the
   standard equation of a line.

9. Find the slope and intercept of a line parallel to Y = 2/3 X + 3
   that passes through (4, 4).

10. Describe the line in #9 using the slope–intercept form, then using the
    standard equation of a line.

Simplify and solve.

11. 8X – 3X + 7 = 4X + 8

12. 4Q + 12 = 20 (Remember the GCF)

13. $5^2 \div 5 + 3(X + 7) = 2X + 27$

14. $7^2 \times 2 - 4(Y + 11) = 3Y - 2$

15. $.6 - \frac{2}{3}X = 11$ (Hint: First change all numbers into fractions.)

16. | –8 – 4 | – 6Y = 32 ÷ | –8 |

For #17–18: Mario's car has a 16–gallon tank. He left for a four–day round trip.

17. Day 1: He left at 7:45 AM and arrived at 2:15 PM after driving 338
      miles. What was his average speed in miles per hour?
      (Tip: Find number of hours and divide that number into 338.)

18. When he left, he had a full tank of gas. At the end of the day, it took
      13 gallons to refill his tank. How many miles per gallon did he get?
      (Tip: Divide the number of miles driven by the number of gallons used.)

19. Fill in the blanks and explain the pattern. 2, 4, 8, 16,____ ,____ ,____

20. Fill in the blanks and explain the pattern.

      0, 1, 1, 2, 3, 5,____ ,____ , 21, 34, 55

Follow the directions.

1. Draw line *a*: Y = $-\frac{1}{2}$ X + 1.
    Label it *a*.

2. Draw line *b*: Y = $-\frac{3}{2}$ X + 5.
    Label it *b*.

3. Record the point where line *a*
    and line *b* intersect.

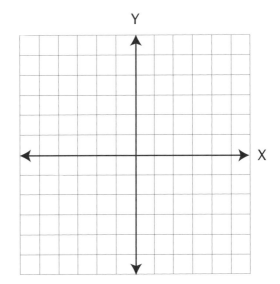

4. **Given:** m = $-\frac{3}{2}$ through the
    point (–1, 1).

    Find the intercept (b).

5. Describe the line in #4 using the
    slope-intercept form, then using
    the standard equation of a line.

6. Find the slope through (–4, 2) and (1, –4) by computing. $\frac{Y_2 - Y_1}{X_2 - X_1}$ = m

7. Find the intercept of the line in #6.

8. Describe the line in #6 using the slope-intercept form, then using the
    standard equation of a line.

9. Find the slope and intercept of a line parallel to Y = $-\frac{4}{3}$ X + 1 that
    passes through (2, –3).

10. Describe the line #9 using the slope-intercept form, then using the
    standard equation of a line.

Simplify and solve.

11. $16X - 8X = 56$

12. $18A - 15 = 24$

13. $(1 - 7)^2 - 8N + 11 = -3$

14. $.78 + .4 = 2X$

15. $.3 + \frac{1}{2}A = 2A - 1.8$

16. $(4 - 8)^2 \times 6 - 3 \times 5^2 = 7Y$

For #17–18: Mario's car has a 16–gallon tank. He left for a four–day round trip.

17. Day 2: He left at 6:50 AM and arrived at 2:05 PM after driving 348 miles. What was his average speed in miles per hour?

18. When he left, he had a full tank of gas. At the end of the day, it took 14.5 gallons to refill his tank. How many miles per gallon did he get?

19. Fill in the blanks and explain the pattern.

    1, 4, 9, 16, 25, ___ , ___ , ___ , ___ , 100

20. Fill in the blanks and explain the pattern.

    1/2, 1/6, 1/18, 1/54, ___ , ___ , ___

Follow the directions.

1. Draw line *a*: $Y = \dfrac{1}{3} X + 2$.
   Label it *a*.

2. Draw line *b*: $Y = 2X - 3$.
   Label it *b*.

3. Record the point where line
   a and line *b* intersect.

4. **Given:** m = 1 through the point
   (5, 2). Find the intercept (b).

5. Describe the line in #4 using the
   slope–intercept form, then using
   the standard equation of a line.

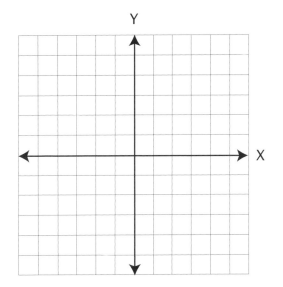

6. Find the slope through (3, 5) and (1, 4) by computing. $\dfrac{Y_2 - Y_1}{X_2 - X_1} = m$

7. Find the intercept in #6.

8. Describe #6 using the slope-intercept form, then using the
   standard equation of a line.

9. Find the slope and intercept of a line parallel to $Y = \dfrac{5}{4} X$
   that passes through (-2, -2).

10. Describe the line in #9 using the slope–intercept form, then using
    the standard equation of a line.

Simplify and solve.

11. $3Q + 7 + 2Q - 5 - 4Q = -Q + 1 + Q + 4$

12. $T + 4 + 3T - 6 - 2T = 2T + 5 - 4T - 1 + 2T$

13. $-2.8P + .06P = 5.72$ 14. $32Y - 8Y = -36$

15. $(.03)(\frac{3}{4})(X) - .75 = 0$ 16. $4\frac{2}{3} + 3\frac{1}{3}X = -3$

For #17–18: Mario's car has a 16-gallon tank. He left for a four-day round trip.

17. Day 3: He left at 8:20 AM and arrived at 2:40 PM after driving 335 miles. What was his average speed in miles per hour?

18. When he left, he had a full tank of gas. At the end of the day, it took 13.4 gallons to refill his tank. How many miles per gallon did he get?

19. Fill in the blanks and explain the pattern.

XA, XB, XC, ___ , ___ , ___

20. Fill in the blanks and explain the pattern.

4.25, 4.5, ___ , ___ , ___ , 5.5, ___ , 6.0

If you can solve one inequality, then you can solve two inequalities. This method is similar to that used to solve simultaneous equations by graphing.

Follow the instructions.

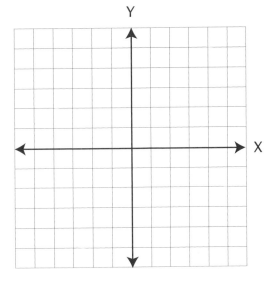

Given: X – Y ≥ 2
           X + Y ≤ 6

1.   Graph the first inequality. Shade the answer in one color or with slanted lines going in one direction.

2.   Graph the second inequality. Shade the answer in another color or with slanted lines going in the opposite direction.

3.   The answers that satisfy both inequalities lie in the region where the two colors or shadings overlap. Will the point (3, –4) satisfy both inequalities given above?

Given: 2X – Y < 2
          3X + Y > 6

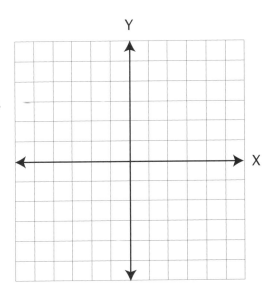

4.   Graph the first inequality. Shade the answer in one color or with slanted lines going in one direction.

5.   Graph the second inequality. Shade the answer in another color or with slanted lines going in the opposite direction.

6.   Will the point (–1, 2) satisfy both inequalities?

Here is a way to use graphs of inequalities to make inventory decisions. Tasty Water, Inc. sells two models of water purifiers. Because demand for model A is high, at least twice as many of model A are stocked as model B. One model A costs the store $200, and a model B costs the store $500. Management policy states that no more than $10,000 worth of the two models should be in inventory at any time. Also, at least five of model A and two of model B should be in stock at all times.

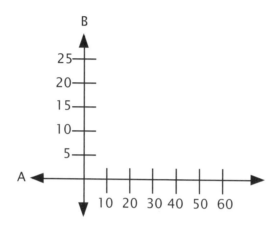

7. Write four inequalities that describe the inventory requirements.

    For example: A ≥ 2B because there must be at least twice as many of model A.

8. Graph all four inequalities, using a different color for each.

9. From the diagram, give one legitimate solution for the numbers of A and B to purchase.

Follow the directions for each set of equations. The first set is done for you.

For #1–3   X = Y + 6, X + 3Y = -2

1. Draw each line and estimate the solution.

   Each line must be changed
   to slope–intercept form.

   First equation:
   X – 6 = Y   Y = X – 6

   Second equation:
   3Y = –X – 2   Y = –1/3 X – 2/3

   Estimated solution is (4, –2)

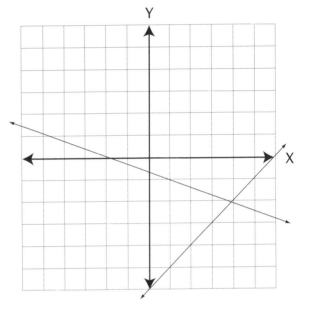

2. Use the substitution method to find Y.

   Go back to the original equations
   and observe that we know X is the
   same as Y + 6. We can replace X in
   the second equation with (Y + 6):
   (Y + 6) + 3Y = –2

   Simplifying and solving as
   usual, we find that Y = (–2)

3. Using the solution to #2, substitute to find X.
   We can substitute in either equation, but the first one looks easier.
   X = (–2) + 6   X = 4

For #4–6   2X + 3Y = 0, X – 2Y = 7

4. Draw each line and estimate
   the solution.

5. Use the substitution method to find Y.
   You must first solve one of the
   equations for X.

6. Using the solution to #5,
   substitute to find X.

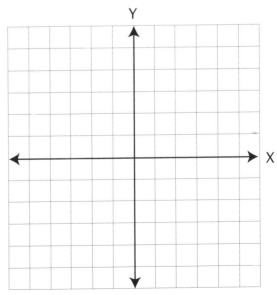

For #7–9   Y = 2X – 5, X + 2Y = 10

7. Draw each line and estimate the solution.

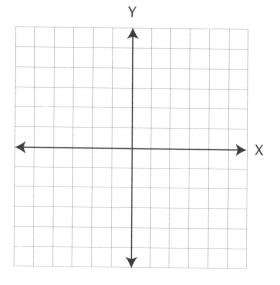

8. Use the substitution method to find X.

    This time you are looking for another way to express Y. The first equation tells us that Y = 2X – 5, so we substitute that value for Y in the second equation:

    X + 2(2X – 5) = 10

9. Using the solution to #8, substitute to find Y.

For #10   2X – 3Y = –4, Y = X + 3

10. Use the substitution method to solve the equations.

    You may find X or Y first. Choose the one that will require less manipulation of the equations.

Follow the directions for each set of equations.

For #1-3   X + Y = 1, Y = X + 3

1. Draw each line and estimate the solution.

2. Use the substitution method to find Y.

3. Using the solution to #2, substitute to find X.

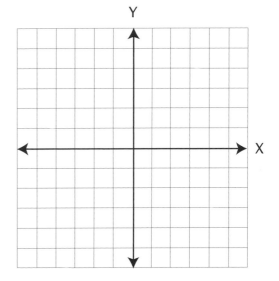

The Y–intercept for one of the next lines is off the graph. See if you can figure out how to graph without being able to see the Y–intercept. If you can't, use a larger piece of graph paper.

For #4-6   2X – Y = 4, Y = -X + 11

4. Draw each line and estimate the solution.

5. Use the substitution method to find Y.

6. Using the solution to #5, substitute to find X.

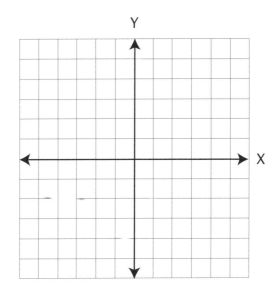

For #7-9   2X + Y = -1, Y = -3X

7. Draw each line and estimate the solution.

8. Use the substitution method to find Y.

9. Using the solution to #8, substitute to find X.

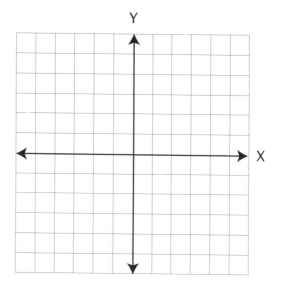

For #10   2X + 3Y = 29, 5X - Y = 30

10. Use the substitution method to solve the equations. First change the second equation to the slope-intercept form.

For #1–3   Y = X + 1 and Y = 2X – 2.

1. Sketch and estimate the solution.

2. Using the substitution method, find X.

3. Using the solution to #2, find Y.

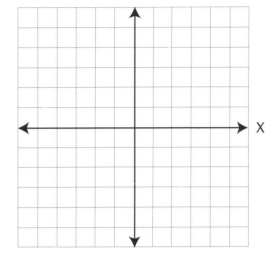

For #4–6   Y – X = 4 and Y + 2X = 1.

4. Sketch and estimate the solution.

5. Using the substitution method, find X.

6. Using the solution to #5, find Y.

7. Find the slope through (4, 5) and (1, 3) by computing. $\dfrac{Y_2 - Y_1}{X_2 - X_1} = m$

8. Find the Y-intercept of the line in #7.

9. Describe the line in #7 using the slope-intercept form, then using the standard equation of a line.

10. Find the slope of a line parallel to $Y = -\dfrac{1}{3}X - 2\dfrac{1}{3}$ that passes through (2, 2).

11. Find the Y-intercept of of the line in #10.

12. Describe the line in #10 using the slope-intercept form, then using the standard equation of a line.

13. Fill in the blanks so that each value in the second line is the same as the value directly above it.

____, 4 , 9 , ____, ____, ____, ____, 64 , ____, ____, 121 , ____, ____, ____, 225

1^2 , ____, ____, 4^2 , ____, ____, ____, ____, 9^2 , 10^2 , ____, ____, ____, ____, 15^2

For #14–16 Use a USA map to find the following information. Assume 25 mpg and 50 mph.

14. Day One: Travel between Seattle and San Francisco. How far will we go?

15. We leave at 7:35 AM and our ETA (estimated time of arrival) is _____.

16. How much gasoline is consumed?
At $1.269 per gallon, how much does it cost?

17. Write 12/13 as a decimal rounded to the nearest thousandth.

18. Distribute: A(2A – A + 3) =

19. Is 97 prime or composite?

20. What is the least common multiple of 6 and 4?

For #1–3   Y = 2X + 6 and X + Y = –6.

1. Sketch and estimate the solution.

2. Using the substitution method, find X.

3. Using the solution to #2, find Y.

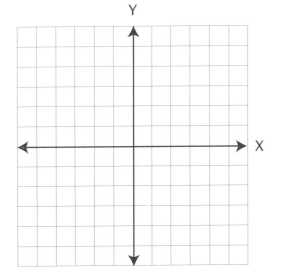

For #4–6   Y + X = –5 and Y – 2X = 4.

4. Sketch and estimate the solution.

5. Using the substitution method, find X.

6. Using the solution to #5, find Y.

7. Find the slope through (0, 0) and (–2, 4) by computing. $\dfrac{Y_2 - Y_1}{X_2 - X_1} = m$

8. Find the Y-intercept of #7.

9. Describe the line in #7 using the slope–intercept form, then using the standard equation of a line.

10. Find the slope of a line perpendicular to $Y = -\dfrac{4}{3} X - 2\dfrac{1}{3}$ that passes through (2, 2).

11. Find the Y-intercept of the line in #10.

12. Describe the line in #10 using the slope–intercept form, then using the standard equation of a line.

13. Fill in the blanks so that each value in the second line is the same as the value directly above it.

1, ____, ____, ____, 25, ____, ____, ____, 81, ____, ____, 144, ____, ____, ____

____, 2^2, ____, ____, ____, 6^2, ____, ____, ____, ____, ____, 12^2, 13^2, ____, 15^2

For #14-16 Use a USA map to find the following information.
Assume 25 mpg and 50 mph.

14. Day Two: Travel between San Francisco and Los Angeles.
How far will we go?

15. We leave at 6:14 AM and our ETA
(estimated time of arrival) is_____ .

16. How much gasoline is consumed?
At $1.199 per gallon, how much does it cost?

17. Write 9/28 as a decimal rounded to the nearest thousandth.

18. Use the GCF to simplify 9A + 27B – 81 = 18C.

19. What are the prime factors of 435?

20. $\sqrt{64}$ =

For #1–3 X + Y = –4 and X – Y = –6.

1. Sketch and estimate the solution.

2. Using the substitution method, find X.

3. Using the solution to #2, find Y.

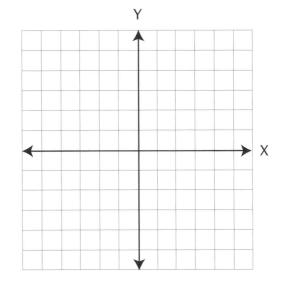

For #4–6 Y – 4X = 4 and Y + 2X = –2.

4. Sketch and estimate the solution.

5. Using the substitution method, find X.

6. Using the solution to #5, find Y.

7. Find the slope through (–1, 1) and (3, –2) by computing. $\dfrac{Y_2 - Y_1}{X_2 - X_1} = m$

8. Find the Y-intercept of #7.

9. Describe the line in #7 using the slope-intercept form, then using the standard equation of a line.

10. Find the slope of a line parallel to Y = 3/5 X – 2 4/5 through (–3, –2).

11. Find the Y–intercept of #10.

12. Describe the line in #10 using the slope–intercept form,
    then using the standard equation of a line.

13. Fill in the blanks so that each value in the second line is the same as the
    value directly above it.

    ____, ____, ____, ____, ____, 36 , ____, ____, ____, 100 , ____, ____, ____, 196 , ____

    ____, ____, 3^2 , ____, ____, ____, ____, 8^2 , ____, ____, 11^2 , ____, ____, ____, ____

For #14–16 Use a USA map to find the following information.
    Assume 25 mpg and 50 mph.

14. Day Three: Travel between Los Angeles and Albuquerque.
        How far will we go?

15. We leave at 4:42 AM and our ETA is _____.
    (Round your answer to the nearest minute.)

16. How much gas is consumed? _____
    At $1.289 per gallon, how much does it cost? _____

17. Write $\dfrac{7}{19}$ as a decimal rounded to the nearest thousandth.

18. Write $\dfrac{9}{10}$ as a percent.

19. Is subtraction associative?   20. 16% of 24.3 =

14H

Write the necessary number of equations and solve the problems.

1. Wheelchair ramp requirements state that the slope for the ramp must not exceed 1/12. Would a nine-inch high ramp that is eight feet long meet the requirements for a wheelchair ramp?

2. How long would a 10-inch high ramp have to be in order to meet the wheel-chair ramp requirements stated in #1?

3. A rectangle is three feet longer than it is wide. Its perimeter is 4.5 times its shorter side. Find its width and length.

Mathematical information can often be expressed in several different ways. In this lesson, we will use a bar graph, an equation, and a Cartesian graph to illustrate the same information.

The bar graph at the right shows actual book sales for the Best Book company.

An equation that models this data is $B = 12T + 42$.

    B = book sales in 1,000s of dollars.
    T = number of years (2000 is year 0).

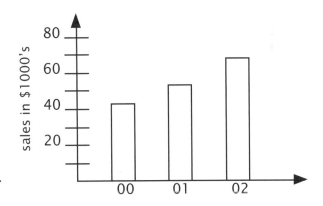

4. If the yearly increase remained the same, what was the amount of sales in 2004?

5. What would be the predicted sales for 2005?

6. In what year would the company expect to sell $126,000 worth of books?

7. Let the X-axis equal the number of years and the Y-axis equal sales amounts. Graph points using the values for 2000 through 2004. (You will need to estimate some points.) Draw the line that includes the points.

   In order to make the information fit conveniently, make each horizontal space represent one year and each vertical space represent $10,000.

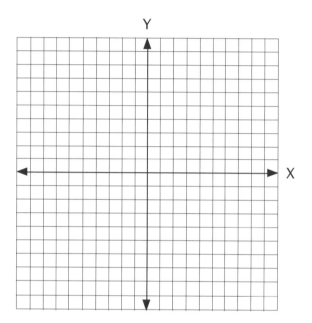

8. Use the Cartesian graph to estimate how many dollars worth of books were sold in 1997. Assume that the rate of growth stayed the same throughout the years.

Follow the directions for each set of equations.

For #1-3 X + Y = -1, 2X + Y = -4

1. Draw each line and estimate the solution.

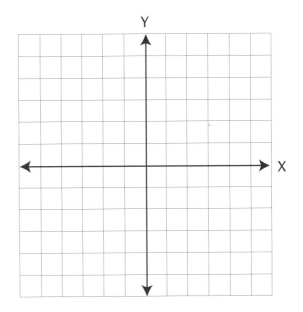

2. Use the elimination method to find X.

3. Using the solution to #2, substitute to find Y.

For #4-6 X + Y = -2, 3X - Y = -2

4. Draw each line and estimate the solution.

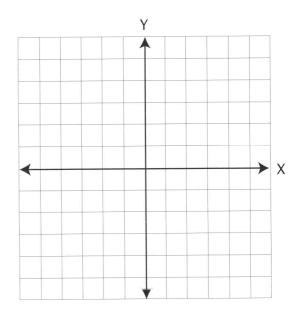

5. Use the elimination method to find X.

6. Using the solution to #5, substitute to find Y.

For #7-9   X − Y = 5, 2X + Y = 7

7. Draw each line and estimate the solution.

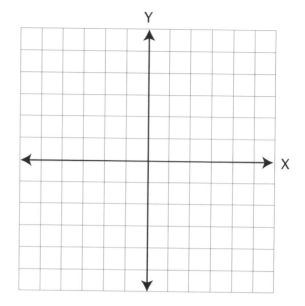

8. Use the elimination method to find X.

9. Using the solution to #8, substitute to find Y.

For #10   4X + Y = 6, 2X + 3Y = 18

10. Use the elimination method to solve the equations.

Follow the directions for each set of equations.

For #1-3   X – Y = 3, 3X – Y = 13

1. Draw each line and estimate the solution.

2. Use the elimination method to find X.

3. Using the solution to #2, substitute to find Y.

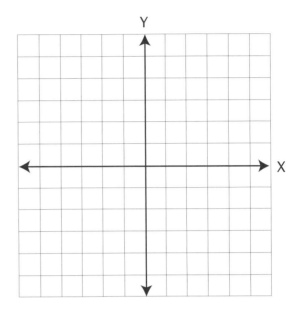

For #4-6   3X – Y = –10, 2X – Y = –8

4. Draw each line and estimate the solution.

5. Use the elimination method to find X.

6. Using the solution to #5, substitute to find Y.

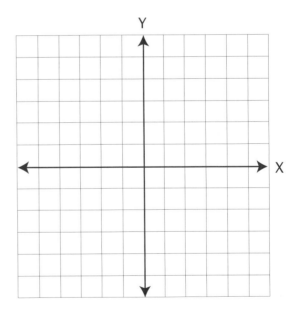

For #7-9 $3X + 2Y = 5, X - Y = 0$

7. Draw each line and estimate the solution.

8. Use the elimination method to find X.

9. Using the solution to #8, substitute to find Y.

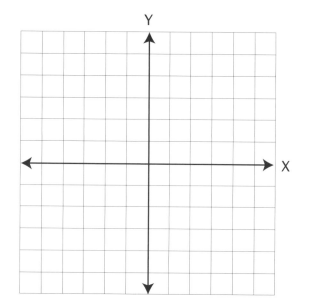

For #10 $X + Y = -3, 3X - Y = -1$

10. Use the elimination method to solve the equations.

For #1-3   2Y + 3X = -2 and 2Y - X = 6

1. Sketch and estimate the solution.

2. Using the elimination method, find Y.

3. Using the solution to #2, find X.

For #4-6   Y + 3X = 2 and Y - X = -2

4. Sketch and estimate the solution.

5. Using the elimination method, find X.

6. Using the solution to #5, find Y.

For #7-9   -2Y > 3X + 6

7. Rewrite using the slope-intercept form.

8. Graph the inequality.

9. Will the point (3, -4) satisfy the inequality?

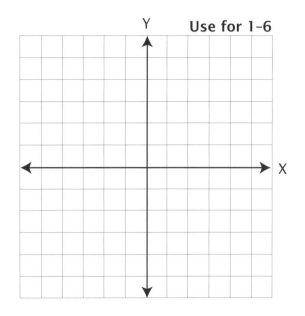

Y   **Use for 1-6**

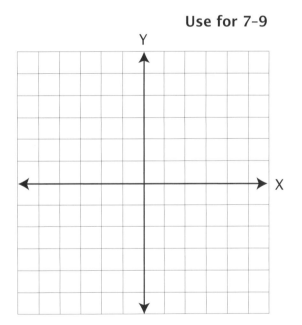

Use for 7-9

Y

10. Find the slope of a line parallel to Y = 1/2 X - 3 through (-1, 1).

11. Find the Y-intercept of the line in #10.

12. Describe the line in #10 using the slope-intercept form,
    then give the equation of the line in standard form.

13. Fill in the blanks in both lines so that the values match.

    ____, ____, ____, 16, ____, 36, ____, ____, 81 , ____, 121, ____, ____, ____, ____

    ____, 2^2, ____, ____, ____, ____, 7^2, ____, ____, ____, ____, ____, 13^2, ____, ____

14. Use algebraic symbols to represent the following: six times a number, minus
    four, equals ten times the number, divided by 2.

15. Solve for the unknown in #14.

16. Use the value of the unknown found in #15 to find the value of this
    expression: $X^2 - 2X + |3 - 4| =$

17. 14% of 25 =   18. WF x 16 = 8

19. 3.14 ÷ 2.4 = (to nearest thousandth)

20. Three fourths divided by five-sixths equals _____

For #1-3   3Y + 2X = 12 and 4Y - X = 5

1. Sketch and estimate the solution.

2. Using the elimination method, find Y.

3. Using the solution to #2, find X.

For #4-6   X + Y = 4 and 2X + Y = 6

4. Sketch and estimate the solution.

5. Using the elimination method, find X.

6. Using the solution to #5, find Y.

For #7-9   5Y ≥ 4X + 10

7. Rewrite using the slope-intercept form.

8. Graph the inequality.

9. Will the polnt (2, 1) satisfy the inequality?

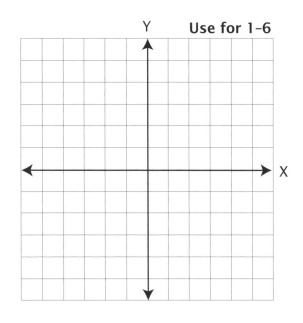

Y   **Use for 1-6**

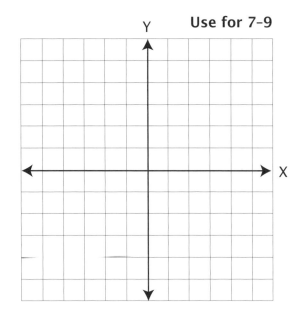

Y   **Use for 7-9**

10. Find the slope of a line perpendicular to $Y = \dfrac{1}{2} X - 3$ through $(-1, 1)$.

11. Find the Y-intercept of the line in #10.

12. Describe the line in #10 using the slope-intercept form, then give the equation of the line in standard form.

13. Fill in the blanks in both lines so that the values match.

    ____, ____, 9, ____, ____, ____, 49, 64, ____, ____, ____, 144, ____, ____, ____

    ____, ____, ____, ____, 5^2, ____, ____, ____, 9^2, ____, 11^2, ____, ____, ____, ____

14. Use algebraic symbols to represent the following: three times a number, minus four times the number, plus eight, equals three times the number.

15. Solve for the unknown in #14.

16. Use the value of the unknown found in #15 to find the value

    of this expression: $3X^2 - X \div |4 - 3| =$

17. 48% of 32 =   18. WF x 75 = 5

19. 21.8 ÷ .4 =

20. Two-sevenths divided by one-half equals ____

For #1–3 Y – X = –3 and Y – 2X = –4

1. Sketch and estimate the solution.

2. Using the elimination method, find Y.

3. Using the solution to #2, find X.

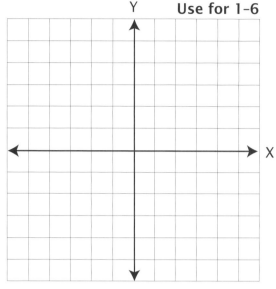

Y   **Use for 1–6**

X

For #4–6 X – 2Y = –5 and X + Y = –2

4. Sketch and estimate the solution.

5. Using the elimination method, find X.

6. Using the solution to #5, find Y.

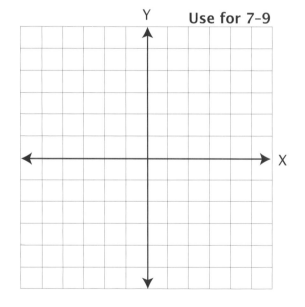

Y   **Use for 7–9**

X

For #7–9 Y < –4 + 3X

7. Rewrite using the slope–intercept form.

8. Graph the inequality.

9. Will the point (2, 3) satisfy the inequality?

10. Find the slope of a line parallel to $Y = 2X - 4$ through $(1, 1)$.

11. Find the Y-intercept of the line in #10.

12. Describe the line in #10 using the slope-intercept form,
    then give the equation of the line in standard form.

13. Fill in the blanks in both lines.

    ____, ____, ____, ____, 25 , ____, ____, ____, ____, 100, ____, ____, ____, ____, 225

    ____, ____, ____, 4^2 , ____, 6^2, ____, 8^2, ____, ____, ____, ____, ____, 14^2 , ____

14. Use algebraic symbols to represent the following: a number minus two,
    plus the number, plus five times the number, equals six
    times the number, plus one.

15. Solve for the unknown in #14.

16. Use the value of the unknown found in #15 to find the value
    of this expression: $5X - 4 + 3X \div 2 =$

17. 150% of 18 =

18. 2/3 of 95 = (to nearest hundredth)

19. 3.14 x 4.16 =

20. Write 9/16 as a decimal rounded to the nearest hundredth.

Write two equations for each problem and solve using whichever method you prefer.

1. Anna can buy a top and a skirt for $62.48. She decides to buy the skirt and two of the tops in different colors. The cost of all three items is $87.98. What is the cost of one top?

2. Tommy bought 10 bags of corn for his animals and five bags of layer pellet for his chickens. The total cost was $85. The next month, Tommy decided to invest in a larger supply of animal feed. He bought 20 bags of corn and eight bags of layer pellet for a total cost of $158. What is the price of one bag of corn? (Assume the prices have not changed.)

3. The cost of one notebook and one pen is $2.00. The cost of two notebooks and three pens is $4.75. What is the cost of one pen?

4. One pond is 180 cm deep. The depth is being reduced by three cm per week. The second pond is 150 cm deep. Its depth is being reduced by two cm per week. In how many weeks will the two ponds have the same depth?

5. A factory employs 700 people. Employees who have worked there less than two years receive an average of $10 an hour. Those who have worked at the factory for two years or more receive an average of $15 an hour. If payroll expenses for one hour are $8,500 (and everyone is at work), how many people have been employed less than two years?

The approach to this problem is a little different from the others in this lesson.

6. I am thinking of two numbers, such that three times the first is one-fourth of twice the second. Find three pairs of numbers that will fit the description.

Follow the directions to find the number of coins.

There are eight coins made up of nickels and dimes. The total value is $.65.

1. Write two equations, one for the number of coins and one for the value.

2. How many dimes are there?

3. How many nickels are there?

There are 25 coins made up of pennies and dimes. The total value is $.88.

4. Write two equations, one for the number of coins and one for the value.

5. How many pennies are there?

6. How many dimes are there?

There are 26 coins made up of nickels and pennies. The total value is $.86.

7. Write two equations, one for the number of coins and one
    for the value.

8. How many nickels are there?

9. How many pennies are there?

There are 13 coins made up of quarters and dimes. The total value is $1.75.

10. Write two equations, one for the number of coins and one
    for the value.

11. How many quarters are there?

12. How many dimes are there?

Follow the directions to find the number of coins.

There are 20 coins made up of nickels and dimes. The total value is $1.75.

1. Write two equations, one for the number of coins and one for the value.

2. How many nickels are there?

3. How many dimes are there?

There are 39 coins made up of pennies and dimes. The total value is $1.83.

4. Write two equations, one for the number of coins and one for the value.

5. How many pennies are there?

6. How many dimes are there?

There are 19 coins made up of nickels and dimes. The total value is $1.25.

7. Write two equations, one for the number of coins and one for the value.

8. How many nickels are there?

9. How many dimes are there?

There are 40 coins made up of quarters and nickels. The total value is $5.00.

10. Write two equations, one for the number of coins and one for the value.

11. How many quarters are there?

12. How many nickels are there?

For #1-3   There are 12 coins made up of nickels and dimes.
The total value is $.85.

1. Write the two equations, one for the number of coins and one
for the value.

2. There are _____ dimes.

3. There are _____ nickels. Check your answers.

For #4-6   There are 10 coins made up of pennies and nickels.
The total value is $.38.

4. Write the two equations, one for the number of coins and one
for the value.

5. There are _____ pennies.

6. There are _____ nickels.
Check your answers.

For #7-8 $3Y - 4X = 2$ and $Y - 2X = -6$

7. Use the elimination method to
find Y.

8. Use the solution to #7 to find X.

9. Find the equation of a line through
(4, 5) and (-3, -2). Graph the line.

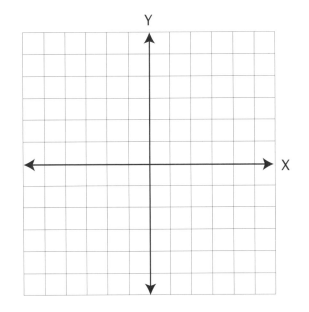

10. Write the equation of a line through (1, -2) and parallel to the line in #9.
Graph the line.

11. Write the equation of a line through (1, -2) and perpendicular to the
line in #9. Graph the line.

12. When first observed, the vine was 24 inches long. Thereafter it grew at a length of two feet per week. Write an equation describing the growth of the vine where X is the number of weeks and Y is the total length.

    (Warning: Be sure your units of measure are the same.)

13. Using your equation from #12, find the length of the vine after three weeks.

14. With the application of fertilizer, the vine will grow three feet per week. Find its length after nine weeks.

15. $(3 + 5) \times (2 - 7) - 3 - 3^2 =$

16. In what quadrant is the point $(6, -7)$?

17. Is subtraction commutative?   18. Is multiplication commutative?

19. $13^2 =$ 20. $\sqrt{64} =$

For #1–3   There are 9 coins made up of nickels and dimes.
The total value is $.60.

1. Write the two equations, one for the number of coins and one for the value.

2. There are _____ dimes.

3. There are _____ nickels. Check your answers.

For #4–6   There are 6 coins made up of pennies and nickels.
The total value is $.26.

4. Write the two equations, one for the number of coins and one for the value.

5. There are _____ pennies.

6. There are _____ nickels.
Check your answers.

For #7–8 $Y - 3X = -1$ and $4Y + 3X = -19$

7. Use the elimination method to find Y.

8. Use the solution to #7 to find X.

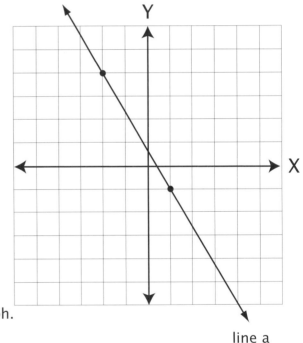

9. Find the equation of line *a* on the graph.

line a

10. Write the equation of a line through (2, 2) and parallel to #9.
Graph the line.

11. Write the equation of a line through (–2, –6) and perpendicular to #9.
Graph the line.

12. Kim started with $4.00 and saved $2.00 a week. Write an equation describing the growth of her savings, using X for the number of weeks and Y for the total dollars she has each week.

13. Ali started with $8.00 and saved $1.00 a week. Write an equation describing the growth of Ali's savings, using X and Y as in #12.

14. You can solve the two equations in #12 and #13 to find out in which week the girls' savings would be equal. Use elimination to find the value of X. This is the week in which they have the same savings.

15. Now solve the two equations for Y, using substitution. This is the dollar amount each girl has in her bank when the amounts are equal.

16. Using your equations from #12 and #13, tell how much each girl would have in the bank after 12 weeks.

17. $-(5 - 9)^2 + (14 - 17)^2 =$

18. In what quadrant is the point $(-3, -3)$?

19. Is division associative?

20. Is multiplication associative?

For #1-3   There are 14 coins made up of nickels and dimes.
The total value is $1.10.

1. Write the two equations, one for the number of coins
and one for the value.

2. There are _____ dimes.

3. There are _____ nickels. Check your answers.

For #4-6   There are 8 coins made up of pennies and nickels.
The total value is $.20.

4. Write the two equations, one for the number of coins
and one for the value.

5. There are _____ pennies.

6. There are _____ nickels.
Check your answers.

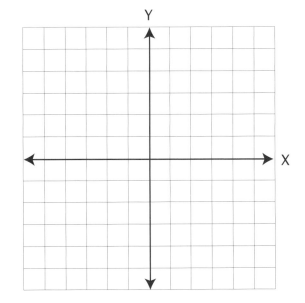

For #7-8   Y = 2X + 2 and Y = -4X - 4

7. Use the substitution method
to find X.

8. Use the solution to #7 to find Y.

9. Graph Y = -3X + 3.

10. Write the equation of a line through (0, 0) and parallel to #9.
Graph the line.

11. Write the equation of a line through (0, 0) and perpendicular to #9.
Graph the line.

12. The temperature of a liquid increases 5°C for every minute it is heated. The temperature was 100°C when the record keeping began. Write an equation describing what happened. Use T for the temperature and M for the minutes.

13. Using your equation from #12, find the temperature of the liquid after 15 minutes.

14. The rate of heating is increased to 10°C every minute. Write a new equation. Now what would the temperature be after 15 minutes?

15. $-[\,7 - (-5)\,]^2 + (3 - 8)^2 =$

16. In what quadrant is the point (–2, 3)?

17. Is addition associative?

18. Is division commutative?

19. $25^2 =$

20. $\sqrt{225} =$

The point where costs and revenue are equal for a business is called the *break-even* point. I think of costs as "out-go," since they are money spent, and revenue as a fancy word for "in-come," which is money coming in.

Read each word problem and answer the questions.

Pam has a mechanical pencil company. Her costs are 12¢ per pencil plus $2,000 startup costs. First let's create hard data and see whether we can observe a pattern. Find the cost of 1,000 pencils, 5,000 pencils, 10,000 pencils, and 20,000 pencils. Then divide the cost by the number of the pencils in each case to find the cost per pencil.

$$(1,000 \times .12) + \$2,000 = \$2,120 \qquad 2,120 \div 1,000 = 2.12$$
$$(5,000 \times .12) + \$2,000 = \$2,600 \qquad 2,600 \div 5,000 = .52$$
$$(10,000 \times .12) + \$2,000 = \$3,200 \qquad 3,200 \div 10,000 = .32$$
$$(20,000 \times .12) + \$2,000 = \$4,400 \qquad 4,400 \div 20,000 = .22$$

1. Write an equation for cost (C) based on the number of pencils sold (N).

2. Pam sells each pencil for 62¢. Write an equation for revenue (R) based on the number of pencils sold (N).

3. How many does she need to sell to break even? At this point Pam's costs and revenue will be equal. Make the equations you wrote for #1 and #2 equal to each other, and solve for N. The answer is the number of pencils Pam must sell in order to break even.

Nicenet, an internet–service provider, is offering two plans for internet service.

Plan 1   Pay a flat fee of $19.95 per month for unlimited service.
Plan 2   Pay $4.95 per month and $2.00 per hour for each hour used.

4. First figure the cost of two hours, six hours, 10 hours, and 14 hours with each plan and look for a pattern.

5. Write an equation for Plan 1 in terms of cost (C) per month. Write an equation for Plan 2 in terms of cost (C) and hours (H) per month.

6. Break-even analysis looks to see where these two plans are equal. Make the two equations you wrote equal to each other, and solve for H to find the break-even point. What can you conclude?

Follow the directions to find the unknown integers.

Find three consecutive integers such that the sum of the integers plus four is equal to four times the second integer.

1. Represent each integer with an unknown.

2. Write an equation using the unknowns.

3. Solve for the three integers.

4. Check by substituting the integers in your equation.

Find three consecutive even integers such that the sum of the first and second integers is equal to the third integer, plus four.

5. Represent each integer with an unknown.

6. Write an equation using the unknowns.

7. Solve for the three integers.

8. Check by substituting the integers in your equation.

Find three consecutive integers such that five times the second integer is equal to three times the sum of the other two, plus two.

9. Represent each integer with an unknown.

10. Write an equation using the unknowns.

11. Solve for the three integers.

12. Check by substituting the integers in your equation.

Find three consecutive odd integers such that the first plus the third is equal to three times the second, plus three.

13. Represent each integer with an unknown.

14. Write an equation using the unknowns.

15. Solve for the three integers.

16. Check by substituting the integers in your equation.

Follow the directions to find the unknown integers.

Find three consecutive even integers such that three times the third is equal to twice the sum of the first and second, plus two.

1. Represent each integer with an unknown.

2. Write an equation using the unknowns.

3. Solve for the three integers.

4. Check by substituting the integers in your equation.

Find three consecutive integers such that the sum of the first and third is equal to twenty times the second.

5. Represent each integer with an unknown.

6. Write an equation using the unknowns.

7. Solve for the three integers.

8. Check by substituting the integers in your equation.

Find three consecutive integers such that five times the first integer plus twice the second is equal to six times the third.

9. Represent each integer with an unknown.

10. Write an equation using the unknowns.

11. Solve for the three integers.

12. Check by substituting the integers in your equation.

Find three consecutive odd integers such that the first plus the third is equal to three times the second plus nineteen.

13. Represent each integer with an unknown.

14. Write an equation using the unknowns.

15. Solve for the three integers.

16. Check by substituting the integers in your equation.

For #1-3   Find three consecutive even integers such that five times the third, minus four times the first, is the same as four times the second.

1. Represent each integer with an unknown.

2. Write an equation using the unknowns.

3. Solve for the three integers.

For #4-6   Find three consecutive integers such that six times the second, plus four times the first, is the same as nine times the third, minus four.

4. Represent each integer with an unknown.

5. Write an equation using the unknowns.

6. Solve for the three integers.

7. Eleven coins made up of dimes and nickels have a value of $.80. Solve and check your answer.

For #8-10   Y – 5 > 4X – 9

8. Rewrite using the slope–intercept form.

9. Graph the inequality.

10. Does the point (1, 2) satisfy the inequality?

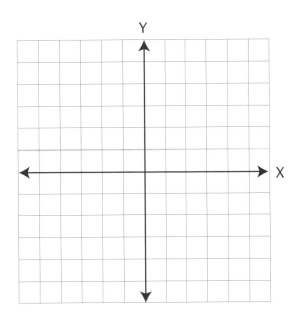

11. Line 1: $4Y + X = 11$ Using the substitution or
    Line 2: $2Y - 3X = 9$ elimination method, find X and Y.

12. What is the equation of a line parallel to line 1 in #11 through (0, 1)?

13. What is the least common multiple of 3 and 7?

14. Use algebraic symbols to represent the following: the sum of a number and two, multiplied by four, equals twenty–three, plus the number.

15. Solve for the unknown in #14.

16. Use the value of the unknown found in #15 to find the value of this expression: $[2(X - 3) + 1] \div X$.

17. One-half plus two-thirds equals _____ .

18. $75\% \times 250 =$

19. Solve: $1.8 - .16A = 10$

20. What are the prime factors of 96?

For #1-3 Find three consecutive odd integers such that four times the third, plus one, is the same as three times the first, plus two times the second.

1. Represent each integer with an unknown.

2. Write an equation using the unknowns.

3. Solve for the three integers.

For #4-6 Find three consecutive integers such that three times the first, minus five times the second, is the same as negative one.

4. Represent each integer with an unknown.

5. Write an equation using the unknowns.

6. Solve for the three integers.

7. Fifteen coins made up of dimes and nickels have a value of $1.10. Solve and check your answer.

For #8-10 Y + 2 > X

8. Rewrite using the slope-intercept form.

9. Graph the inequality.

10. Does the point (–4, –3) satisfy the inequality?

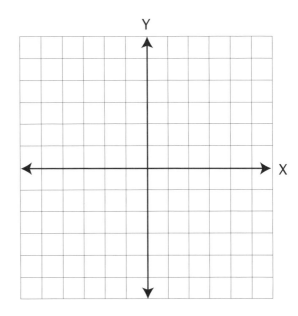

11. Line 1: 5Y + 6X = –19   Using the substitution or
    Line 2: 5Y + 3X = –22   elimination method, find X and Y.

12. What is the equation of a line perpendicular to line 1 in #11 through (–4, 1)?

13. What is the least common multiple of 6 and 8?

14. Use algebraic symbols to represent the following: two times a number, minus six, plus eight times the number, equals four.

15. Solve for the unknown in #14.

16. Use the value of the unknown found in #15 to find the value of this expression: $3X - X^2 + 13 - 4X$.

17. One-sixth plus three-fourths equals _____ .

18. 13% x 180 =

19. Solve: 6A – 16 – 4A = 20

20. What are the prime factors of 135?

For #1-3   Find three consecutive even integers, such that five times the first, plus three times the third, is the same as seven times the second, plus ten.

1. Represent each integer with an unknown.

2. Write an equation using the unknowns.

3. Solve for the three integers.

For #4-6   Find three consecutive integers such that seven times the third, minus five times the second, is the same as four times the first, plus one.

4. Represent each integer with an unknown.

5. Write an equation using the unknowns.

6. Solve for the three integers.

7. Seven coins made up of dimes and quarters have a value of $1.00. Solve and check your answer.

For #8-10 $-1/2\ Y - 2 \leq X - 4$

8. Rewrite using the slope-intercept form.

9. Graph the inequality.

10. Does the point (4, 4) satisfy the inequality?

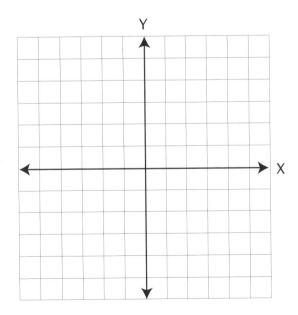

11. Line 1: $Y - 3X = -4$
    Line 2: $Y + X = 0$

    Using the substitution or elimination method, find X and Y.

12. What is the equation of a line parallel to line 1 in #11 through (2, –2)?

13. What is the least common multiple of 15 and 25?

14. Use algebraic symbols to represent the following: two times the sum of one and negative eight, equals eighteen, minus two times a number.

15. Solve for the unknown in #14.

16. Use the value of the unknown found in #15 to find the value of this expression: $3Y - 5 + 6Y + (10 - 6)$.

17. Two-sevenths minus one-fourteenth equals _____ .

18. $120\% \times 100 =$

19. Solve: $.5X + 1.5 = 4.5$

20. What are the prime factors of 102?

Here is another example of finding the break–even point.

Read the problem and answer the questions.

Hometown Bank is offering a new business checking account for $10 per month plus 10¢ per check after the first 50 checks. Ameribank is offering a competitive program for $8 per month plus 12¢ per check after the first 50 checks. Assume you will write at least 50 checks per month.

1. Write an equation for each bank's program. Use F for the monthly fee and C for the number of checks.

2. What is the break-even point at which both plans cost the same?

3. If your company writes an average of 110 checks a month, which plan would be cheaper?

Here is another problem similar to those in lesson 11 involving linear equations.

Read the problem and answer the questions.

A new home in a nearby subdivision is estimated to cost $30,000 plus $75 for each square foot of floor space in the house.

4. Write an equation for the cost (C) of a new home with "S" square feet of floor space.

5. How much would a new home with 2,000 square feet of living area cost?

6. How many square feet can you afford if you have $150,000 to spend?

Simplify each expression.

1. $15^2 =$

2. $\sqrt{169} =$

3. $(-8)^2 =$

4. $-\sqrt{100} =$

5. $16^2 =$

6. $\sqrt{144} =$

7. $4^5 \cdot 4^2 =$

8. $8^4 \cdot 8^7 =$

9. $8^7 \div 8^3 =$

10. $3^8 \cdot 3^4 =$

11. $B^2 B^3 B^5 =$

12. $C^1 D^5 D^4 C^3 D^2 =$

13. $8^X \cdot 8^Y =$

14. $M^{10X} \div M^{3X} =$

15. $8^9 \cdot 8^{10} \div 8^3 =$

16. $X^{5Y} \div X^{2Y} =$

Simplify each expression.

1. $25^2 =$

2. $2^3 =$

3. $(-9)^2 =$

4. $(7)^3 =$

5. $(-17)^2 =$

6. $-\sqrt{81} =$

7. $5^3 \cdot 5^6 =$

8. $6^4 \cdot 6^2 =$

9. $18^{13} \div 18^9 =$

10. $4^8 \cdot 4^5 =$

11. $(4^2) =$

12. $C^1 \, C^2 \, C^3 =$

13. $F^3 \, F^4 \, E^5 \, F^2 =$

14. $B^6 \, C^1 \, C^3 \, B^7 =$

15. $Y^{10} \cdot Y^5 \div Y^3 =$

16. $A^{8X} \div A^{3X} =$

Simplify each expression.

1. $14^2 =$

2. $\sqrt{121} =$

3. $(-9)^2 =$

4. $-\sqrt{49} =$

5. $3^3 \cdot 3^3 =$

6. $5^2 \cdot 5^6 =$

7. $6^5 \div 6^2 =$

8. $4^5 \cdot 4^2 =$

9. $A^5 A^2 B^4 B^1 =$

10. $B^Y \cdot B^{2Y} =$

11. $A^5 \div A^1 =$

12. $X^5 \cdot X^2 \div X^7 =$

13. When you multiply two numbers with the same base, you _____ the exponents.

14. When you divide two numbers with the same base, you _____ the exponents.

For #15–16   Find three consecutive integers such that five times the third, minus two times the first, is the same as four times the second, minus forty.

15. Write the equation using unknowns.

16. Solve the equation to find the integers.

17. Twenty nickels and dimes have a value of $1.60. How many are there of each coin?

18. Write 6X + 3Y = 10 in the slope–intercept form.

For #19–20   A nursery has a two-foot sapling and a four-foot sapling. The two-foot sapling will grow at a rate of three feet a year, but the four-foot sapling will grow at only one foot a year. In how many years will the saplings be the same height? How tall will they be then?

19. Write two equations using X for the number of years and Y for the height of the saplings.

20. Use substitution or elimination to solve for X and Y and answer the questions.

Simplify each expression.

1. $-13^2 =$

2. $-\sqrt{144} =$

3. $(-15)^2 =$

4. $\sqrt{100} =$

5. $7^3 \cdot 7^4 \cdot 7 =$

6. $2^8 \cdot 2^3 \cdot 2^2 =$

7. $X^2 \cdot X^9 =$

8. $A^4 A^5 B^2 =$

9. $8^5 \div 8^3 =$

10. $10^5 \div 10 =$

11. $X^{10} \div X^4 =$

12. $X^{4Y} \cdot X^{3Y} \div X^Y =$

13. When you _____ two numbers with the same base, you subtract the exponents.

14. When you _____ two numbers with the same base, you add the exponents.

For #15-16   Find three consecutive odd integers such that four times the second, plus three times the third, is the same as eight times the first, minus eleven.

15. Write the equation using unknowns.

16. Solve the equation to find the integers.

17. Seven quarters and dimes have a value of $1.60. How many are there of each coin?

For #18-20   A craftsman has orders for special Christmas ornaments. He already has 30 finished and can make 37 a week.

18. Write an equation with X as the number of weeks and Y for the total number of ornaments needed.

19. If he needs a total of 215 ornaments, how many weeks must he work?

20. With new orders, the craftsman must now make 326 ornaments. How many weeks will it take to finish?

Simplify each expression.

1. $-11^2 =$

2. $\sqrt{196} =$

3. $7^2 =$

4. $-\sqrt{225} =$

5. $A^2 \cdot A^4 =$

6. $5^3 \cdot 5^4 =$

7. $A^2 B^3 B^6 A^1 C^2 =$

8. $X^4 \div X^3 =$

9. $9^9 \div 9^3 =$

10. $11^4 \cdot 11^6 =$

11. $D^{3X} \div D^{2X} =$

12. $M^5 \cdot M^3 \div M^3 =$

13. $\sqrt{100}$ is equal to _____ , and $-\sqrt{100}$ is equal to _____ .

14. When you multiply two or more numbers with the _____ _____, you add the exponents.

For #15-16   Find three consecutive even integers such that four times the second is equal to three times the first, plus three times the third.

15. Write the equation using unknowns.

16. Solve the equation to find the integers.

17. Ten quarters and dimes have a value of $1.75. How many are there of each coin?

18. Write Y = –4X + 16 in the standard form of an equation of a line.

For #19-20   Worker 1 has made 50 gizmos and can work at a rate of 25 gizmos an hour. Worker 2 has already made 200 gizmos, but his rate is only 10 an hour. How many hours will it be until they have the same number made? How many gizmos will each worker have in all when their output is equal?

19. Write two equations using X for the number of hours and Y for the total number of gizmos.

20. Use substitution or elimination to solve for X and Y and answer the questions.

The first three problems are similar to consecutive-integer problems. Choose a letter to represent the smallest unknown in the problem. Write the other unknowns in terms of that letter, or variable. Write an equation showing the relationship between the various terms as you did for consecutive-integer problems. After solving for the chosen variable, use your answer to find the other unknown values.

Write an equation and solve.

1. Billy's piggy bank contains only nickels, dimes, and quarters. The number of nickels is three times the number of dimes. The number of quarters is four more than the number of nickels. There are 18 coins in all. Find the number of quarters in the piggy bank.

2. Best Showing Movie Theatre has three ticket prices. Senior citizens pay $5, other adults pay $8, and children pay $4 each. On the night that an historical documentary of World War II was shown, the theatre took in $1,120 in ticket sales. There were four times the number of senior citizens as children. The number of children was one-half the number of adults. How many paying customers saw the movie that night?

3 Super Suites Hotel has four rates for its 250 basic rooms. Senior citizens pay $35 a night. Businesses pay $45, and coupon-holders pay $40. The standard rate is $50 per night if none of these other rates apply. On New Year's Eve, the hotel's room rates brought in $8,640 in income.

   The number of rooms sold to senior citizens that night was 10 fewer than the number of standard rooms. The number of business rooms was eight fewer than the number of coupon-holder rooms sold. Also, the sale of coupon-holder rooms was 10 times less than the number of standard rooms sold. How many rooms were empty on New Year's Eve at Super Suites?

4. The local post office's supply of stamps is low. There are $5.70 worth of stamps left in the drawer in only three denominations – 1¢, 20¢, and 37¢. There are five fewer 20¢ stamps than 37¢ stamps. There are 10 times the number of 1¢ stamps as 37¢ stamps. How many 1¢ stamps does the post office have?

Hint: Set up like a coin problem, substituting stamp denominations for coin denominations.

Each of the problems below is a variation on coin problems. Set up each problem and make all the substitutions. You should eventually have two equations and two unknowns that you can solve as simultaneous equations.

5. A local caterer charges variable fees for its wedding dinners. Men are charged $10, women $8, and children $5. Fifteen people were served at a particular meal. The number of men served was one more than the number of women served. If the bill came to $112, how many children were served?

6. The digits of a two-digit number add up to 10. If the digits are reversed, the new number is 36 larger than the original number. What is the original number?

Hint: Label each digit of the original number as a separate variable.

Write on one line.

1. $\dfrac{1}{4^2} =$

2. $\dfrac{1}{7^2} =$

3. $\dfrac{1}{4^{-3}} =$

4. $\dfrac{1}{3^{-2}} =$

Rewrite using positive exponents.

5. $5^{-3} =$

6. $10^{-7} =$

Simplify each expression and write it on one line.

7. $7^{-3} \cdot 7^{-8} =$

8. $6^{-2} \cdot 6^{-3} =$

9. $9^{-5} \div 9^{-2} =$

10. $3^8 \cdot 3^4 =$

Simplify each expression and write it on one line.

11. $B^{-2} B^3 C^{-1} B^5 C^{-5} C^1 =$

12. $C^{-1} D^{-5} D^4 C^3 D^{-2} D^4 C^1 =$

13. $(8^5)^4 =$

14. $(9^3)^5 =$

15. $\dfrac{A^{-1} B^2 B^{-1}}{AB^{-3}} =$

16. $\dfrac{C^0 B^{-3} C^3 B}{C^{-3} B^4} =$

Write on one line.

1. $\dfrac{1}{8^{-2}} =$

2. $\dfrac{1}{5^3} =$

Rewrite using positive exponents.

3. $7^{-1} =$

4. $X^{-6} =$

Simplify each expression and write it on one line.

5. $4^{-8} \cdot 4^5 =$

6. $6^{-4} \cdot 6^{-2} =$

7. $(3^{-3})^2 =$

8. $(A^4)^{-5} =$

9. $(4^{-2})^3 =$

10. $C^0 D^{-5} D^6 C^1 C^2 C^3 =$

Simplify each expression and write it on one line.

11. $E^0 F^3 F^4 E^{-5} F^{-2} E^{-6} =$

12. $B^{-6} C^1 C^2 C^3 C^{-4} B^7 =$

13. $Y^{-10} \cdot Y^5 \div Y^3 =$

14. $A^{8X} \div A^{3X} =$

15. $\dfrac{X^{-5}Y^2X^3Y^2}{Y^{-3}Y^4X^2} =$

16. $\dfrac{A^{-3}B^2A^5B^3}{B^4A^{-3}A^5} =$

Simplify as directed.

1. Write on one line: $\dfrac{1}{3^2}$

2. Rewrite using positive exponents: 2^{-4}

3. Write on one line: $\dfrac{1}{7^{-2}}$

4. Rewrite using positive exponents: Y^{-5}

Simplify each expression and write it on one line.

5. $4^5 \cdot 4^{-2} =$

6. $5^{-2} \cdot 5^{-6} =$

7. $A^{-8} B^{-2} A^3 A^4 B^5 =$

8. $D^{-2} C^3 C^4 D^4 C^{-2} D^4 =$

9. $4^{-10} \cdot 4^6 =$

10. $X^5 \div X^4 =$

11. $(3^3)^2 =$

12. $(2^5)^7 =$

13. $(-8)^2 =$

14. $\sqrt{25} =$

15. $\dfrac{E^{-1}F^2F^3E^4}{F^{-2}E^{-3}E^5} =$

16. What number is this? $1 \times 10^3 + 3 \times 10^2 + 7 \times 10^0 + 8 \times 10^{-2}$
    (This is exponential notation.)

For #17–18: Find three consecutive odd integers such that three times the first
integer, plus four times the second, equals negative thirteen times
the third integer.

17. Write the equation using unknowns.

18. Solve the equation to find the integers.

19. Seven nickels and dimes have a total value of $.45.
    How many are there of each coin?

20. Write 5X + 10Y – 20 = 0 in the slope–intercept form.

SYSTEMATIC REVIEW

Simplify as directed.

1. Write on one line: $\dfrac{1}{4^{-5}}$

2. Rewrite using positive exponents: 5^{-8}

3. Write on one line: $\dfrac{1}{x^5}$

4. Rewrite using positive exponents: A^{-1}

Simplify each expression and write it on one line.

5. $X^A \cdot X^B =$

6. $3^{-2} \cdot 3^8 =$

7. $E^0 \, F^5 \, E^{-1} \, F^{-2} \, E^3 \, F^3 =$

8. $C^{-8} \, B^5 \, C^1 \, C^2 \, B^{-6} \, C^4 =$

9. $7^{-3} \div 7^{-6} =$

10. $X^{10Y} \div X^{5Y} =$

11. $(10^3)^4 =$

12. $(1{,}000^5) = 10^?$

13. $-5^2 =$

14. $-\sqrt{36} =$

15. $\dfrac{C^5 D^4 D^{-3}}{D^{-2} C^1 C^{-3} D^4} =$

16. What number is this? $2 \times 10^4 + 5 \times 10^1 + 6 \times 10^{-1} + 9 \times 10^{-2}$

For #17–18: Find three consecutive even integers such that three times the first integer, plus six times the second, equals eight times the third, minus fourteen.

17. Write the equation using unknowns.

18. Solve the equation to find the integers.

19. Eleven quarters and dimes have a total value of $2.15. How many are there of each coin?

20. Solve for X and Y: Y – X = 0, Y – 3X = -4

Simplify as directed.

1. Write on one line: $\dfrac{1}{7^{-3}}$

2. Rewrite using positive exponents: 10^{-7}

3. Write on one line: $\dfrac{1}{A^X}$

4. Rewrite using positive exponents: 8^{-X}

Simplify each expression and write it on one line.

5. $A^2 \cdot A^{-4} =$

6. $5^6 \div 5^4 =$

7. $10^{11} \cdot 10^{-3} \div 10^5 =$

8. $D^2 \, C^{-3} \, C^{-4} \, D^8 \, C^2 \, D^{-4} =$

9. $M^{-X} \cdot M^X =$

10. $X^{2Y} \div X^{4Y} =$

11. $[\,(11^2)^5\,]^3 =$

12. $(49)^3 = 7^?$

13. $(15)^2 =$

14. $\sqrt{81} =$

15. $\dfrac{X^1 Y^2 X^4 Y^{-1}}{X^{-3} Y^4} =$

16. Represent this number with exponential notation: 4.093

For #17–18: Find three consecutive integers such that two times the first integer, plus three times the second, minus the third, is equal to twenty–one.

17. Write the equation using unknowns.

18. Solve the equation to find the integers.

19. Thirty quarters and nickels have a total value of $4.30. How many are there of each coin?

20. Write Y = –2X + 9 using the standard form of the equation of a line.

You have solved problems that can be represented by a straight line on a graph. These problems can be written in the form $AX + BY = C$ and do not involve exponents. When amounts in a problem increase exponentially, we get a very different kind of graph.

Follow the directions to make a graph of an exponential increase.

1. A scientist starts with 1,000 bacteria in a dish. The number of bacteria doubles every three hours. Fill in the missing values to make a chart of the first 24 hours of bacterial growth.

t (hours)	0	3	6	9	12	15	18	21	24
b (bacteria in thousands)	1	2	4						

Notice that starting with 2, each value of b can be written as 2 with an exponent.

2. Plot the points from the chart on the graph below, and connect them with a *curved* line showing the growth in numbers of bacteria. (Estimate the location of the value of b for each point.)

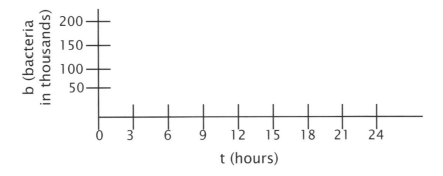

3. A new bacterial culture also begins with 1,000 bacteria. This time the number of bacteria doubles every hour. Fill in the chart for the first 12 hours. How many bacteria will there be after 12 hours?

t (hours)	0	1	2	3	4	5	6	7	8	9	10	11	12
b (bacteria in thousands	1	2	4										

4. Plot the points from the chart on the graph below, and connect them with a curved line.

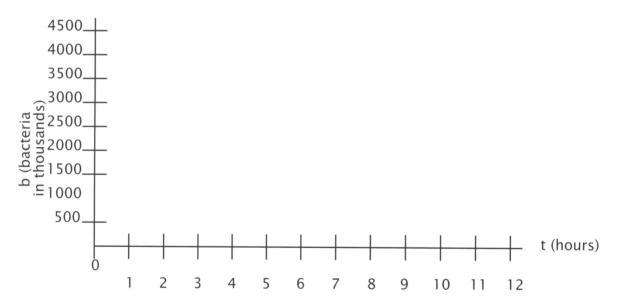

5. As values increase exponentially, what do you notice about the rate of increase over time?

ALGEBRA 1

Build.

1. $X^2 + 11X + 2$ 2. $X^2 + 6X + 8$ 3. $X^2 - 8$

Build and add.

4. $X^2 - 6X + 3$
     $+ \; 3X^2 + 7X - 9$

5. $X^2 \qquad\quad - 8$
     $+ \; X^2 + 6X - 7$

6. $2X^2 + 10X + 7$
     $+ \; 2X^2 - 8X \; - 9$

Build a rectangle and find the area (product).

7. $(X + 1)(X + 2) =$

8. $(X + 4)(X + 3) =$

9. $(X + 1)(X + 5) =$

Multiply.

10.
$$\begin{array}{r} 3X + 2 \\ \times\ \ X + 1 \\ \hline \end{array}$$

11.
$$\begin{array}{r} 5X + 5 \\ \times\ \ X + 2 \\ \hline \end{array}$$

12.
$$\begin{array}{r} 2X + 1 \\ \times\ \ X + 5 \\ \hline \end{array}$$

13.
$$\begin{array}{r} X + 8 \\ \times\ 3X + 5 \\ \hline \end{array}$$

14.
$$\begin{array}{r} X + 3 \\ \times\ 2X + 1 \\ \hline \end{array}$$

15.
$$\begin{array}{r} 3X + 2 \\ \times\ 2X + 1 \\ \hline \end{array}$$

16.
$$\begin{array}{r} 4X + 2 \\ \times\ \ X + 3 \\ \hline \end{array}$$

17.
$$\begin{array}{r} 2X - 5 \\ \times\ \ X + 2 \\ \hline \end{array}$$

18.
$$\begin{array}{r} 3X + 5 \\ \times\ 3X - 1 \\ \hline \end{array}$$

Build.

1. $X^2 - 3X - 7$

2. $2X^2 - 7X - 3$

3. $X^2 + 5X + 9$

Build and add.

4. $X^2 + 3X + 2$
   $+ X^2 + 7X + 12$

5. $X^2 + 6X + 5$
   $+ 3X^2 - X - 2$

6. $5X^2 - 5X - 10$
   $+ 2X^2 + 11X + 5$

Build a rectangle and find the area (product).

7. $(X + 4)(X + 5) =$

8. $(X + 7)(X + 3) =$

9. $(X + 4)(X + 8) =$

Multiply.

10.
$$
\begin{array}{r}
7X + 1 \\
\times \ \ X + 2 \\
\hline
\end{array}
$$

11.
$$
\begin{array}{r}
3X + 7 \\
\times \ \ X + 6 \\
\hline
\end{array}
$$

12.
$$
\begin{array}{r}
2X + 8 \\
\times \ 3X + 1 \\
\hline
\end{array}
$$

13.
$$
\begin{array}{r}
X + 8 \\
\times \ X - 3 \\
\hline
\end{array}
$$

14.
$$
\begin{array}{r}
2X - 1 \\
\times \ \ X + 9 \\
\hline
\end{array}
$$

15.
$$
\begin{array}{r}
3X + 5 \\
\times \ \ X + 2 \\
\hline
\end{array}
$$

16.
$$
\begin{array}{r}
4X - 2 \\
\times \ \ X - 3 \\
\hline
\end{array}
$$

17.
$$
\begin{array}{r}
5X + 2 \\
\times \ 3X - 3 \\
\hline
\end{array}
$$

18.
$$
\begin{array}{r}
3X + 7 \\
\times \ 4X + 2 \\
\hline
\end{array}
$$

Build and add.

1. $3X^2 + 7X + 6$
   $+ \ X^2 + 2X + 3$

2. $2X^2 + 5X + 1$
   $+ \ \ \ X^2 + 3X + 4$

3. $4X^2 + 8X + 2$
   $+ \ -X^2 + 3X - 1$

Build a rectangle and find the area (product).

4. $(X + 4)(X + 8) =$

5. $(X + 5)(X + 2) =$

6. $(X + 2)(X + 6) =$

Multiply.

7. $3X + 6$
   $\times \ \ X + 2$

8. $2X + 5$
   $\times \ \ X + 3$

9. $4X - 5$
   $\times \ \ X + 1$

10. Write on one line: $\dfrac{1}{X^{-4}}$

11. Rewrite using positive exponents: X^{-3}

Simplify. Write expressions with exponents on one line.

12. $5^2 \times 3^0 \times 5^{-4} =$

13. $A^4 \div A^7 =$

14. $(5^2)^5 =$

15. $(5)^{12} = (5^3)^{?} =$

16. $\sqrt{196}$ =

17. $C^{-5} \times C^2$ =

18. The base of a rectangle is X + 4, and the height is X + 5. What is the area of the rectangle? (Remember that the area of a rectangle is base times the height.)

19. Find the area of the rectangle in #18 if X equals six.

20. Take two times the base and height of the rectangle in #18, using the distributive property, and then find the polynomial that expresses the new area.

Build and add.

1. $X^2 - 3X - 7$
   $+ 2X^2 + 4X - 4$

2. $X^2 + 11X + 2$
   $+ 3X^2 - 4X + 6$

3. $X^2 - 10X - 5$
   $+ -2X^2 - X + 14$

Build a rectangle and find the area (product).

4. $(X + 2)(X + 7) =$

5. $(2X + 3)(X + 4) =$

6. $(X + 1)(X + 9) =$

Multiply.

7. $2X + 4$
   $x \quad X + 3$

8. $3X - 1$
   $x \quad X + 4$

9. $2X - 3$
   $x \quad X - 4$

10. Write on one line: $\dfrac{1}{X^4}$

11. Rewrite using positive exponents: $\dfrac{1}{Y^{-5}}$

Simplify. Write expressions with exponents on one line.

12. $3^7 \times 4^3 \times 4^{-2} =$

13. $B^5 \div B^1 =$

14. $(8^3)^6 =$

15. $(2)^{15} = (2^3)^? =$

16. $\sqrt{225} =$

17. $D^{-3} \times D^8 \times D^{-7} =$

18. The base of a rectangle is 2X + 4, and the height is X + 4. What is the area of the rectangle?

19. Find the area of the rectangle in #18 if X equals 10.

20. The area of a second rectangle is $X^2 + 3X + 1$. What is the sum of the area of the two rectangles (from #18 and #20)?

Build and add.

1. $X^2 + 3X - 2$
   $+ \ X^2 + 4X + 3$

2. $3X^2 + 2X - 1$
   $+ \ 2X^2 - 2X + 8$

3. $5X^2 + 4X + 7$
   $+ \ -X^2 + 3X + 7$

Build a rectangle and find the area (product).

4. $(X + 3)(X + 3) =$

5. $(2X + 4)(X + 2) =$

6. $(3X)(X + 2) =$

Multiply.

7. $2X - 3$
      x $X - 2$

8. $X - 1$
      x $X - 6$

9. $2X + 2$
      x $X - 3$

10. Write on one line: $\dfrac{1}{X^5}$

11. Rewrite using positive exponents: Y^{-2}

Simplify. Write expressions with exponents on one line.

12. $7^{-2} \times 7^5 \div 7^{-2} =$

13. $A^7 \div B^3 =$

Simplify. Write expressions with exponents on one line.

14. $(5^2)^5 =$

15. $(5)^{12} = (5^3)^? =$

16. $-\sqrt{169} =$

17. $C^0 C^{-4} D^8 D^{-7} D^{-3} C^3 =$

18. Stephanie's savings are represented by $3N + 4$, and Chuck's are represented by $2N + 5$. Write an expression representing their combined savings.

19. Stephanie and Chuck have each been saving as described in #18 for 10 weeks (N), what is the total amount they have saved?

20. The base of a rectangle is $2Y + 7$, and the height is $7Y + 5$. What is the area of the rectangle?

Here are some more problems involving exponents.

Follow the directions and answer the questions.

1. Suppose that m represents the mass in grams of a substance that halves in size each month. You can find the value for each month simply by dividing the value for the previous value by two.

x (number of months)	0	1	2	3	4
m (mass in grams)	200				

2. What was the mass of the substance when measuring began? (time = 0)

3. How long will it be until there are 100 grams remaining?

4. How long will it be until there are only 50 grams remaining?

5. What is the mass of the substance after four months?

6. Make a graph showing the first five months of decrease of the substance described on the previous page.

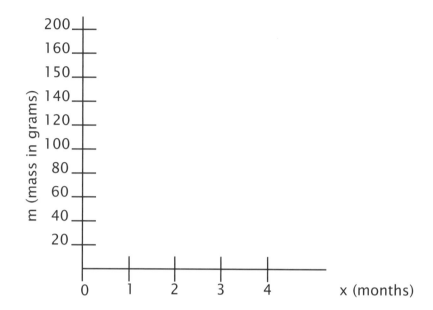

In real life, a scientist may wish to find the value of m for a certain number of months without finding every value in between. In this case, $m = 200(.5)^x$, where x stands for the number of months. Compare the example to the corresponding value on your chart.

Example $m = 200(.5)^x$. Find the value of m after four months.
$m = 200(.5)^4$ $m = 200(.0625) = 12.5$ grams

7. Use the equation given above to find the mass of the substance after six months.

Build a rectangle and find the factors. Check by multiplying.

1. $X^2 + 4X + 4$

2. $X^2 + 5X + 6$

3. $X^2 + 11X + 10$

4. $X^2 + 6X + 8$

5. $X^2 + 8X + 7$

6. $X^2 + 8X + 12$

7. $X^2 + 12X + 11$

8. $X^2 + 7X + 6$

9. $X^2 + 9X + 14$

10. $X^2 + 16X + 15$

11. $X^2 + 3X + 2$

12. $X^2 + 4X + 3$

13. $X^2 + 9X + 8$

14. $X^2 + 19X + 18$

15. $X^2 + 9X + 20$

16. $X^2 + 10X + 21$

Find the factors and check by multiplying. (You will not have enough blocks to build some of these.)

1. $X^2 + 10X + 16$

2. $X^2 + 11X + 28$

3. $X^2 + 13X + 22$

4. $X^2 + 7X + 12$

5. $X^2 + 8X + 15$

6. $X^2 + 11X + 30$

7. $X^2 + 5X + 4$

8. $X^2 + 6X + 5$

9. $X^2 + 8X + 16$

10. $X^2 + 12X + 20$

11. $X^2 + 11X + 18$

12. $X^2 + 17X + 30$

13. $X^2 + 7X + 10$

14. $X^2 + 2X + 1$

15. $X^2 + 10X + 25$

16. $X^2 + 26X + 25$

Build a rectangle and find the factors.

1. $X^2 + 7X + 12 = ($ $+$ $)($ $+$ $)$

2. $X^2 + 10X + 16 = ($ $+$ $)($ $+$ $)$

3. $X^2 + 11X + 24 = ($ $+$ $)($ $+$ $)$

4. $X^2 + 8X + 12 = ($ $+$ $)($ $+$ $)$

Build a rectangle and find the area (product).

5. $(X + 4)(X + 2) =$

6. $(X + 5)(X + 3) =$

7. Find the factors: $X^2 + 7X + 6$.

8. Check #7 by multiplying the factors to find the product.

9. Find the factors: $X^2 + 2X + 1$.

10. Check #9 by multiplying the factors to find the product.

Add.

11. $2X^2 - 7X - 3$
    $+ X^2 + 5X + 9$

12. $6X^2 + 2X + 1$
    $+ X^2 - 4X + 3$

When simplifying expressions with exponents, write your answer on one line unless otherwise instructed.

13. Simplify: $(P^{-4})^2 P^3 P^1$

14. Simplify: $(R^{-2}S^3)^{-3}$

15. $15^2 =$

16. $\sqrt{16} =$

17. Find three consecutive odd integers such that eleven times the first, plus two times the second, equals six times the third, plus one.

18. Nine coins made up of dimes and nickels have a total value of $.60. How many are there of each coin?

19. Express using the standard form of the equation of a line: $Y = 7X + 3$.

20. Graph: $4Y < 3X - 5$.

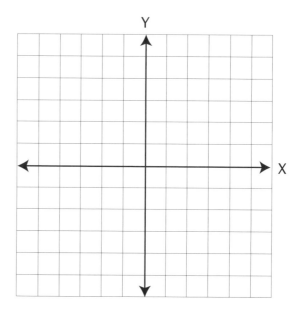

Build a rectangle and find the factors.

1. $X^2 + 11X + 28 = ($ $+$ $)($ $+$ $)$

2. $X^2 + 4X + 4 = ($ $+$ $)($ $+$ $)$

3. $X^2 + 6X + 8 = ($ $+$ $)($ $+$ $)$

4. $X^2 + 8X + 16 = ($ $+$ $)($ $+$ $)$

Build a rectangle and find the area (product).

5. $(X + 5)(X + 1) =$

6. $(X + 3)(X + 3) =$

7. Find the factors: $X^2 + 12X + 32$.

8. Check #7 by multiplying the factors to find the product.

9. Find the factors. $X^2 + 20X + 100$.

10. Check #9 by multiplying the factors to find the product.

Add.

11. $X^2 + X - 4$
   $+ X^2 + 3X + 3$

12. $2X^2 + 7X + 6$
   $+ 5X^2 - 4X + 10$

13. Simplify: $[(P^5)^3]^{-2}$

14. Simplify: $(S^6 R^{-3} S^2)^0$

15. $11^2 =$

16. $\sqrt{144} =$

17. Find three consecutive odd integers such that fourteen times the second, plus four times the first, equals twelve times the third, minus two.

18. Twenty-seven coins made up of dimes and nickels add up to a total of $1.80. How many are there of each coin?

19. Graph the line $Y = 3/2\ X - 1$.

20. Graph a line perpendicular to the line in #19 that passes through (3, -3).

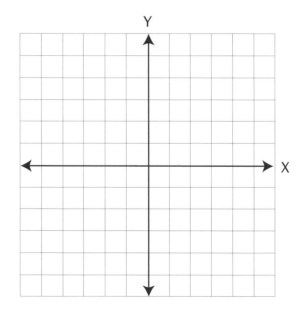

Build a rectangle and find the factors.

1. $X^2 + 8X + 7 = ($ $+$ $)($ $+$ $)$

2. $X^2 + 5X + 6 = ($ $+$ $)($ $+$ $)$

3. $X^2 + 9X + 20 = ($ $+$ $)($ $+$ $)$

4. $X^2 + 8X + 15 = ($ $+$ $)($ $+$ $)$

Build a rectangle and find the area (product).

5. $(X + 1)(X + 9) =$

6. $(X + 7)(X + 2) =$

7. Find the factors: $X^2 + 7X + 12$.

8. Check #7 by multiplying the factors to find the product.

9. Find the factors: $X^2 + 10X + 21$.

10. Check #9 by multiplying the factors to find the product.

Add.

11. $4X^2 - 4X + 1$
     $+ X^2 + 2X - 1$

12. $2X^2 + 3X + 3$
     $+ X^2 + 7X - 2$

13. Simplify: $(P^3)^0 \, P^4 P^{-1}$

14. Simplify: $(S^2 \, R^0 \, S^0)^{-2} \, R^5$

15. $13^2 =$

16. $\sqrt{25} =$

17. Find three consecutive integers such that the second, plus seven times the third, equals five times the first.

18. Twenty coins made up of pennies and nickels add up to $.76. How many are there of each coin?

19. Rewrite in slope-intercept form: $4Y + 3X = 16$.

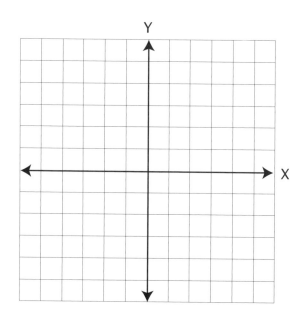

20. Graph: $2Y \geq 3X - 2$.

An exponential equation for growth can be written as follows: $B = A \cdot 2^{\frac{x}{d}}$

> B = the number of bacteria
> A = the beginning population
> d = doubling time
> x = elapsed time

Be sure that you use the same units of time for *x* and *d*. You might want to check this formula with the problems on bacterial growth in honors lesson 19. See whether you get the same results as on the charts you filled in.

Use the growth equation to answer the questions. The first one is done for you.

1. If 10 bacteria cells double every five minutes, how many bacteria will there be in 10 minutes?

   A = 10, d = 5 minutes, and x = 10 minutes,

   so $B = 10 \cdot 2^{\frac{10}{5}} \rightarrow B = 10 \cdot 2^2 \rightarrow B = 10 \cdot 4 = 40$

   After 10 minutes, there will be 40 bacteria cells.

2. If 10 bacteria cells double every five minutes, how many bacteria will there be in 30 minutes?

3. If 10 bacteria cells double every five minutes, how many bacteria will there be in one hour?

4. Make a graph showing the first hour of bacterial growth described on previous page.

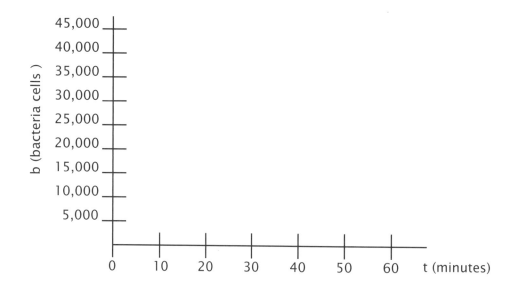

Build and find the factors, then check by multiplying.
Don't forget to look for a greatest common factor first.

1. $2X^2 + 3X + 1$

2. $3X^2 + 13X + 4$

3. $4X^2 + 8X + 4$

4. $2X^2 + 11X + 5$

5. $2X^2 + 15X + 18$

6. $3X^2 + 7X + 2$

7. $2X^2 + 9X + 10$

8. $4X^2 + 10X + 4$

9. $2X^2 + 9X + 9$

10. $4X^2 + 9X + 2$

11. $3X^2 + 10X + 8$

12. $2X^2 + 14X + 20$

13. $2X^2 + 7X + 3$

14. $4X^2 + 7X + 3$

15. $2X^2 + 13X + 18$

16. $3X^2 + 13X + 12$

Build and find the factors, then check by multiplying. Don't forget to check for a GCF.
(You may not have enough blocks to build some of these.)

1. $2X^2 + 7X + 5$

2. $5X^2 + 17X + 6$

3. $2X^2 + 11X + 5$

4. $4X^2 + 13X + 3$

5. $2X^2 + 16X + 30$

6. $3X^2 + 9X + 6$

7. $2X^2 + 11X + 9$

8. $3X^2 + 23X + 14$

9. $2X^2 + 13X + 15$

10. $5X^2 + 50X + 105$

11. $6X^2 + 36X + 48$

12. $3X^2 + 14X + 16$

13. $4X^2 + 14X + 6$

14. $5X^2 + 7X + 2$

15. $10X^2 + 11X + 1$

16. $4X^2 + 23X + 15$

Build a rectangle and find the factors.

1. $3X^2 + 7X + 4 = ($ + $)($ + $)$

2. $2X^2 + 7X + 6 = ($ + $)($ + $)$

Build a rectangle and find the area (product).

3. $(2X + 2)(X + 3) =$

4. $(2X + 4)(X + 2) =$

5. Find the factors: $3X^2 + 13X + 12$.

6. Check #5 by multiplying the factors to find the product.

7. Find the factors: $4X^2 + 24X + 36$.

8. Check #7 by multiplying the factors to find the product.

9. Find the factors: $4X^2 + 8X + 3$.

10. Check #9 by multiplying the factors to find the product.

Simplify. Write your answer on one line unless otherwise instructed.

11. $B^2 \times B^6 \times B^{-5} =$

12. $A^B \cdot A^C =$

Hint for #13-14: first rewrite so that all the terms are in the numerator.

13. $\dfrac{X^{-3}Y^2X^{-1}}{Y^{-3}X^{-5}} =$

14. $\dfrac{A^3A^{-2}B^1}{B^{-2}A^4} =$

15. What number is this? $6 \times 10^6 + 8 \times 10^4 + 2 \times 10^3 + 7 \times 10^{-2}$

16. Rewrite in slope-intercept form and graph: $2Y = 3X - 2$.

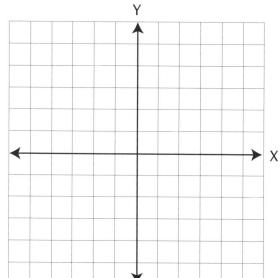

17. What is the equation of a line parallel to #16 through (0,4)? Graph the line.

18. A scientist had one amoeba in a lab dish. The amoeba divided and doubled its numbers every hour. How many are there at the end of one hour?   two hours?   three hours?   four hours?

19. Rewrite each answer in #18 using 2 and an exponent. (At the end of the first hour, there would be 2^1 amoebas.) Look for the pattern.

20. Using exponents, write expressions telling how many amoebas there are after six hours and after X hours.

Build a rectangle and find the factors.

1. $3X^2 + 11X + 10 = ($ $+$ $)($ $+$ $)$

2. $4X^2 + 10X + 4 = ($ $)($ $+$ $)($ $+$ $)$

Build a rectangle and find the area (product).

3. $(3X + 3)(X + 2) =$

4. $(3X)(2X + 1) =$

5. Find the factors: $3X^2 + 8X + 5$.

6. Check #5 by multiplying the factors to find the product.

7. Find the factors: $4X^2 + 11X + 7$.

8. Check #7 by multiplying the factors to find the product.

9. Find the factors: $X^2 + 5X + 6$.

10. Check #9 by multiplying the factors to find the product.

Simplify each expression.

11. $C^{-4} \times C^3 \times C^0 =$

12. $8^5 \div 8^3 =$

Hint for #13–14: first rewrite so that all the terms are in the numerator.

13. $\dfrac{B^5 B^2 C^{-5}}{B^{-4} C^{-3}} =$

14. $\dfrac{D^6 C^{-4} D^2}{D^{-4} C^0 C^2} =$

15. Write this number with exponential notation: 86,900.4

16. Rewrite in slope-intercept form and graph: $3Y = 2X + 6$.

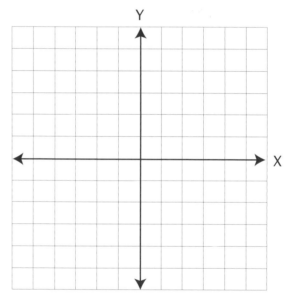

17. What is the equation of a line parallel to #16 through (–3, –3)? Graph the line.

18. Dad agreed to triple Jason's allowance every week. For week one Jason received $3. How much did he get for week two? week three? week four? week five?

19. Rewrite each answer for #18 using 3 and an exponent. (For the first week, Jason would get 3^1 dollars.) Do you see a pattern?

20. Using exponents, write an expression telling how much Jason would be getting per week at the end of 20 weeks. If you have a calculator that will do exponents, use it to find how much money that would be.

Build a rectangle and find the factors.

1. $4X^2 + 12X + 9 = ($ $+$ $)($ $+$ $)$

2. $2X^2 + 12X + 16 = ($ $)($ $+$ $)($ $+$ $)$

3. $(2X + 2)(X + 1) =$ 4. $(2X + 4)(X + 5) =$

Build a rectangle and find the area (product).

5. Find the factors: $4X^2 + 11X + 6$.

6. Check #5 by multiplying the factors to find the product

7. Find the factors: $2X^2 + 11X + 5$.

8. Check #7 by multiplying the factors to find the product.

9. Find the factors: $X^2 + 4X + 3$.

10. Check #9 by multiplying the factors to find the product.

Simplify each expression.

11. $B^2 B^6 C^2 B^{-5} C^{-5} =$

12. $Y^5 \cdot Y^A =$

Hint for #13–14: first rewrite so that all the terms are in the numerator.

13. $\dfrac{D^8 C^{-3} A^{-2}}{A^0 D^{-7} C^2} =$

14. $\dfrac{A^5 D^{-6} A^{-7}}{C^{-3} D^{-8}} =$

15. What number is this? $3 \times 10^5 + 5 \times 10^0 + 2 \times 10^{-2} + 8 \times 10^{-3}$

16. Rewrite in slope–intercept form and graph: $5Y + 4X = 10$.

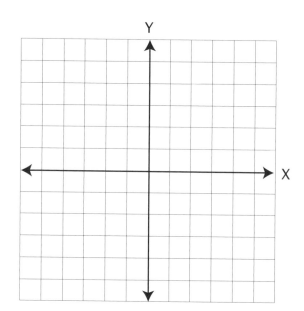

17. What is the equation of a line perpendicular to #16 through (1, –2)? Graph the line.

18. A scientist had one gram of a culture. It increased in weight by a factor of five every day. What did it weigh by the end of one day? two days? three days? four days?

19. Rewrite each answer for #18 using 5 and an exponent. (At the end of the first day, there would be 5^1 grams of culture.)

20. Using exponents, write expressions telling how much the culture would weigh after eight days and after Y days.

Use the following exercise to check your understanding of operations with exponents.

Examine each of the statements. Next to the statement write "always true," "never true," or "sometimes true."

1. $3^{-2} = 9$ _____

2. $X^{-2} = 9$ _____

3. $(2 + 5)^{-1} = 1/2 + 1/5$ _____

4. $\dfrac{2}{X^0} = 0$ _____

5. $(4 - X)^0 - 1 = 0$ _____

6. $8^{-1} = -8$ _____

7. $(XY)^2 (XY)^{-2} = 1$ _____

8. $(B^X)^{2X} = B^{2X^2}$ _____

Graphing exponential equations requires some computation, making a chart, and plotting the points.
Follow the directions.

9. **Given:** $Y = 2^X + 3$.
   Find the value of Y for each value of X, and fill in the chart.

X	Y
0	
1	
2	
−1	
−2	

10. Plot the points from the chart on the graph and connect them with a curved line.

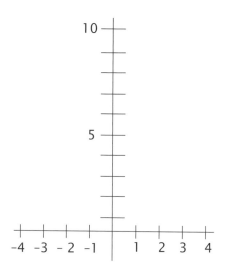

Notice that as the X values get larger, the Y values get larger very quickly (exponentially). As the X values get smaller, the Y values get closer and closer to 3.

Factor each polynomial and check by multiplying.

1. $X^2 - 7X + 10$

2. $X^2 - 7X + 6$

3. $X^2 - 9X + 14$

4. $X^2 - 7X + 12$

5. $X^2 - 9X + 8$

6. $X^2 - 10X + 21$

7. $X^2 - 12X + 27$

8. $X^2 - 11X + 30$

9. $X^2 - 19X + 90$

10. $X^2 - 14X + 33$

11. $X^2 + 4X - 21$

12. $X^2 + 2X - 35$

13. $X^2 + 3X - 18$

14. $X^2 - 5X - 36$

15. $2X^2 - 9X - 5$

16. $2X^2 + 5X - 12$

Factor each polynomial and check by multiplying.

1. $X^2 - 6X + 8$

2. $X^2 - 18X + 80$

3. $X^2 - 8X + 15$

4. $X^2 - 9X + 20$

5. $X^2 - 10X + 9$

6. $X^2 - 4X + 3$

7. $X^2 - 16X + 55$

8. $X^2 - 20X + 96$

9. $X^2 - 13X + 42$

10. $X^2 - 11X + 24$

11. $X^2 + 2X - 3$

12. $X^2 + 3X - 18$

13. $X^2 - X - 20$

14. $X^2 + 2X - 15$

15. $5X^2 + 9X - 2$

16. $4X^2 + 7X - 2$

Build a rectangle and find the factors.

1. $X^2 - 3X - 10 = ($ $- $ $)($ $+$ $)$

2. $X^2 + 3X - 4 = ($ $- $ $)($ $+$ $)$

Build a rectangle and find the area (product).

3. $(X - 3)(X - 9) =$

4. $(X - 3)(X - 3) =$

5. Find the factors: $X^2 + X - 2$.

6. Check #5 by multiplying the factors to find the product.

7. Find the factors: $X^2 + 3X - 10$.

8. Check #7 by multiplying the factors to find the product.

9. Find the factors: $2X^2 + 7X + 3$.

10. Check #9 by multiplying the factors to find the product.

Simplify each expression.

11. $3^4 \times 3^{-2} \div 3^3 =$

12. $\dfrac{7^{-10}}{7^5} =$

13. $\dfrac{A^5 B^2 A^{-4}}{A^3 B^7} =$

Simplify each term, then add like terms.

14. $2AB^{-2} + \dfrac{4B^{-1}}{B^{-1}A^{-1}} + \dfrac{3A^2}{B^2 A^1} =$

15. $3Y = 2X + 7$ and $Y = -4X$.   Solve for both X and Y using substitution.

16. Find three consecutive odd integers such that seven times the second, plus two times the first, minus six times the third, equals negative one.

17. Twelve coins made up of nickels and dimes have a value of $.95. How many are there of each coin?

18. Solve: two-thirds divided by five-sixths times one-half.

19. Solve for X: .2X − .02X + 1.4 = 2.09

20. 5 1/2 % of 400 =   (*Hint:* Change to a decimal, then a percent.)

Build a rectangle and find the factors.

1. $X^2 - X - 2 = ($ $-$ $)($ $+$ $)$

2. $X^2 + 2X - 3 = ($ $-$ $)($ $+$ $)$

Build a rectangle and find the area (product).

3. $(X - 3)(X + 9) =$

4. $(X - 5)(X + 6) =$

5. Find the factors: $X^2 - 3X - 4$.

6. Check #5 by multiplying the factors to find the product.

7. Find the factors: $X^2 - 2X - 3$.

8. Check #7 by multiplying the factors to find the product.

9. Find the factors: $X^2 - X - 6$.

10. Check #9 by multiplying the factors to find the product.

Simplify each expression.

11. $(10^2)^7 =$

12. $[(5^2)^4]^3 =$

13. $\dfrac{D^{-4}D^3D^{-2}}{D^4\,D^{-5}} =$

Simplify each term, then add like terms.

14. $BB^2 + \dfrac{3B^{-1}}{B^{-4}} + \dfrac{5B^4}{B^{-1}} =$

15. $Y = -4X + 5$ and $2Y = 4X - 3$.   Solve for X and Y.

16. Find three consecutive integers such that four times the second, plus three times the third, minus eight times the first, plus eleven, equals zero.

17. Forty-five coins made up of nickels and dimes have a value of $3.30. How many are there of each coin?

18. Solve: one-half divided by one-half times three-fourths.

19. Solve for X: $1.03X + .2X - .73X = .45$

20. $5\dfrac{2}{5}$ % of 250 =

   (*Hint:* Change to a decimal, then a percent.)

Build a rectangle and find the factors.

1. $X^2 - 2X - 3 = ($ $-$ $)($ $+$ $)$

2. $X^2 + 3X - 4 = ($ $-$ $)($ $+$ $)$

Build a rectangle and find the area (product).

3. $(X - 4)(X + 2) =$

4. $(X - 3)(X + 5) =$

5. Find the factors: $X^2 - 7X + 10$.

6. Check #5 by multiplying the factors to find the product.

7. Find the factors: $3X^2 - 10X + 7$.

8. Check #7 by multiplying the factors to find the product.

9. Find the factors: $3X^2 + 15X - 18$.

10. Check #9 by multiplying the factors to find the product.

Simplify each expression.

11. $5^4 \times 5^{-6} \div 5^2 =$

12. $\dfrac{1}{6^{-1}} =$

Simplify each term, then add like terms.

13. $4Q^{-1}Y^{-2} + \dfrac{5QY^{-3}}{Q^{-1}Y^{-2}} =$

14. $5M^4N^2M^{-1} + \dfrac{2NM^4}{N^{-3}M} =$

15. $X - Y = -2$ and $3X + Y = 18$.   Solve for X and Y.

16. Find three consecutive odd integers such that eleven times the first, plus two times the second, equals six times the third, plus one.

17. Fourteen coins made up of quarters and dimes have a value of $2.00. How many are there of each coin?

18. Solve: three-sevenths times fourteen-fifteenths divided by one-half.

19. Solve for F: $36 - 8F = 20F + 12$

20. 6.8% of 95 =

Here are two more exponential equations to graph.

Follow the directions.

1. **Given:** $Y = 2^X + 1$.
    Find the value of Y for each value of X, and fill in the chart.

X	Y
0	
1	
2	
3	
−1	
−2	
−3	

2. Plot the points from the chart on the graph
    and connect them with a curved line.

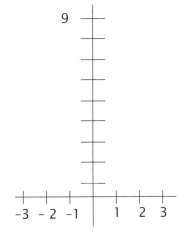

3. What happens to the Y values as the X values get smaller?

4. What happens to the Y values as the X values get larger?

5. **Given:** $Y = 3^X$.

Find the value of Y for each value of X, and fill in the chart.

X	Y
0	
1	
2	
3	
4	
-1	
-2	

6. Plot the points from the chart on the graph and connect them with a curved line.

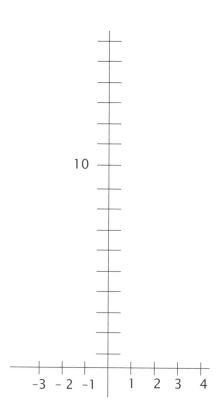

Find the square root and check.

1. $\sqrt{x^2 + 4X + 4}$

2. $\sqrt{x^2 + 6X + 9}$

3. $\sqrt{x^2 + 10X + 25}$

Divide and check.

4. $X + 3 \overline{\smash{\big)}\, x^2 + 5X + 6}$

5. $X + 5 \overline{\smash{\big)}\, x^2 + 11X + 36}$

6. $X + 3 \overline{\smash{\big)}\, x^2 + 7X + 12}$

7. $X + 8 \overline{\smash{\big)}\ X^2 + 10X + 16}$

8. $X + 3 \overline{\smash{\big)}\ X^2 + 10X + 21}$

9. $X + 3 \overline{\smash{\big)}\ 2X^2 + 7X + 3}$

Challenge.

10. $X + 4 \overline{\smash{\big)}\ X^3 + 9X^2 + 27X + 28}$

11. $X + 1 \overline{\smash{\big)}\ X^3 + 4X^2 + 12X + 9}$

Find the square root and check.

1. $\sqrt{x^2 + 12X + 36}$

2. $\sqrt{x^2 + 14X + 49}$

3. $\sqrt{4x^2 + 4X + 1}$

Divide and Check.

4. $X + 3 \overline{\smash{\big)}\, x^2 + 10X + 21}$

5. $X + 2 \overline{\smash{\big)}\, x^2 + 7X + 10}$

6. $X + 1 \overline{\smash{\big)}\, x^2 + 7X + 6}$

7. $X + 3 \overline{\smash{\big)}\, X^2 + 8X + 15}$

8. $X + 4 \overline{\smash{\big)}\, X^2 + 9X + 20}$

9. $X - 2 \overline{\smash{\big)}\, X^2 + X - 6}$

Challenge.

10. $X - 2 \overline{\smash{\big)}\, X^3 - 5X^2 + 11X - 10}$

11. $X - 3 \overline{\smash{\big)}\, X^3 + X^2 - 19X + 26}$

Find the missing factor. Build if necessary.

1. $X + 1 \overline{\smash{\big)}\, 4X^2 + 10X + 1}$

2. Check #1 by multiplication.

3. $2X + 1 \overline{\smash{\big)}\, 4X^2 + 6X + 5}$

4. Check #3 by multiplication.

5. $X + 4 \overline{\smash{\big)}\, X^2 + 9X + 20}$

6. Check #5 by multiplication.

Find the square's factor, or root.

7. $\sqrt{X^2 + 2X + 1} =$

8. Check #7 by multiplication.

Simplify. Write exponent solutions on one line unless otherwise directed.

9. $(X^4)^3 (Y^2)^6 (Y^2)(Y^0) =$

10. $\dfrac{A^5}{A^{-3}} =$

Use only positive exponents in the answer for #12.

11. $X^5 X^{-2} \div X^{-4} =$

12. $2XY^{-1} - \dfrac{3YY^{-2}}{X^{-1}} + 4X^{-1}Y^{-1} =$

Solve.

13. $.234 \times .21 =$

14. $540 \div .15 =$

15. $(-7)(-9) =$

16. $|4 - 8 + 1| =$

Add.

17. $\begin{aligned} 6X^2 - 3X + 2 \\ + \ X^2 + 5X - 1 \end{aligned}$

18. $\begin{aligned} X^2 + 4X - 8 \\ + \ X^2 - 4X - 9 \end{aligned}$

19. What are the factors of 97?

20. Which two operations are commutative?

Find the missing factor. Build if necessary.

1. $X + 1 \overline{) 2X^2 - X + 10}$

2. Check #1 by multiplication.

3. $X + 3 \overline{) 3X^2 + 11X + 6}$

4. Check #3 by multiplication.

5. $X + 4 \overline{) 3X^2 + 10X - 9}$

6. Check #5 by multiplication.

Find the square's factor, or root.

7. $\sqrt{X^2 + 8X + 16} =$

8. Check #7 by multiplication.

Simplify. Write exponent solutions on one line unless otherwise directed.

9. $(A^5 B^7 B^3)^{-2}(A^4) =$

10. $\dfrac{B^4}{AB^{-2}} =$

11. .586 x 1.5 =

12. 125 ÷ 2.5 =

13. (−7) − 9 =

14. $|10 ÷ 2 - 8|$

Add.

15. $7X^2 + 4X − 1$
    $− 2X^2 + 3X + 6$

16. $X^2 + 11X + 5$
    $+ X^2 − 8X − 6$

17. What are the prime factors of 216?

18. Which two operations are associative?

19. Isaac went for a brisk 24-mile walk. Swinging his long arms, he was able to walk six miles per hour. How long did it take him to complete his journey?

20. The next day he was a mite tired. He went for the same 24-mile walk. Swinging his weary arms, he was able to walk only three miles per hour. How long did it take him to complete this journey?

Find the missing factor. Build if necessary.

1. $2X + 2 \overline{)\, 2X^2 + 10X + 8}$

2. Check #1 by multiplication.

3. $X + 4 \overline{)\, 3X^2 + 10X - 8}$

4. Check #3 by multiplication.

5. $2X - 5 \overline{)\, 4X^2 - 2X - 17}$

6. Check #5 by multiplication.

Find the square's factor, or root.

7. $\sqrt{X^2 + 6X + 9} =$

8. Check #7 by multiplication.

Simplify or solve.

9. $(4)^3 = 2^?$

10. $\dfrac{\left(X^4 Y^{-2}\right)^3}{X^3 Y^5 X^{-1}} =$

Use only positive exponents in your answer to #12.

11. $(10)^4 = (10^1)^?$

12. $3A^2B^3A + \dfrac{6A^3B^3}{A^{-1}} - 7B^3A^3 =$

13. $1.68 + .045 =$

14. $49 \div .007 =$

Add.

15. $\quad 2X^2 + 4X - 6$
   $\underline{+ \; X^2 + \; X - 10}$

16. $\quad 5X^2 + 11X - 3$
   $\underline{- \; 4X^2 - \; 5X + 7}$

17. What are the prime factors of 132?

18. What is the GCF of 20XY and 14X?

19. Ethan went for a quick 18-mile bike ride. Pedaling doggedly, he was able to ride at a rate of nine miles per hour. How long did it take him to complete his journey?

20. The next day he walked the same 18 miles. He was able to walk only three miles per hour. How long did it take him that day?

Here are a couple of applications using polynomials.

Follow the directions.

1. Find a polynomial that represents the total number of square feet in the floor plan shown below.

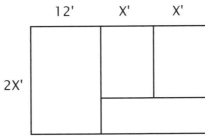

2. If X = 10, how many square feet of floor space are there in this cottage?

3. The base of a triangle is (Y + 1) feet. The height is (2Y – 1) feet. Find the area of the triangle in terms of Y.

Polynomials can have larger exponents and more terms than those in your text. For example:

$X^7 - 2X^6 + X^4 - 3$ is a seventh-degree polynomial. The degree is the value of the highest exponent. Notice that some exponent values are missing (X^5, X^3, X^2, and X^1).

Also, notice that the terms are written in order of decreasing powers of the exponents. Addition and multiplication are performed in the same way as for smaller degree polynomials.

EXAMPLE Add $(X^7 - 3) + (X^6 + 2)$. Set up vertically:

$$\begin{array}{r} X^7 \quad\ - 3 \\ +\quad X^6 + 2 \\ \hline X^7 + X^6 - 1 \end{array}$$

Note carefully that you may only add terms with the same exponents.

Set up vertically and add.

4. $(2X^5 - 3X^4 + 7X) + (X^8 - 2X^4 + 3X)$

5. $(6X^4 + 8) + (2X^9 - 3X^5 - 7X^4 + 4X - 2)$

6. $(5X^3 - 7) + (6X^4 - 5X^3 + 7)$

Multiply vertically or by using the FOIL method. Use the rules for multiplying exponents.

EXAMPLE $(X^3 + 2X)(5X^4 + X^2)$

Set up vertically: $5X^4 + X^2$
$$\underline{\times\ X^3 + 2X}$$
$$10X^5 + 2X^3$$
$$\underline{5X^7\ +\ X^5}$$
$$5X^7 + 11X^5 + 2X^3$$

7. $(2X^2 + 7)(3X^3 + X)$ 8. $(4X^5 + 3)(X^2 - 2)$

9. $8X^4(7X^5 - 2X^3 + 3)$

Find the factors and check by multiplying.

1. $X^2 - 4 =$

2. $X^2 - 16 =$

3. $X^2 - 25 =$

4. $Y^2 - 144 =$

5. $X^2 - 100 =$

6. $X^2 - 81 =$

7. $X^2 - 49 =$

8. $X^2 - 64 =$

9. $A^2 - 121 =$

10. $X^2 - Y^2 =$

11. $B^2 - 4 =$

12. $X^2 - 9 =$

13.
$$\begin{array}{r} 65 \\ \times\, 65 \\ \hline \end{array}$$

14. $35^2 =$

15.
$$\begin{array}{r} 48 \\ \times\, 42 \\ \hline \end{array}$$

16.
$$\begin{array}{r} 85 \\ \times\, 85 \\ \hline \end{array}$$

25B

Find the factors and check by multiplying.

1. $X^2 - 1 =$

2. $X^2 - 36 =$

3. $Y^2 - 16 =$

4. $A^2 - B^2 =$

5. $A^2 - 49 =$

6. $B^2 - 25 =$

7. $Y^2 - X^2 =$

8. $X^2 - 4 =$

303

9. $A^2 - 144 =$

10. $4X^2 - 4Y^2 =$

11. $B^2 - 64 =$

12. $X^2 - 81 =$

13.
$$\begin{array}{r} 57 \\ \times\,53 \\ \hline \end{array}$$

14. $75^2 =$

15.
$$\begin{array}{r} 35 \\ \times\,35 \\ \hline \end{array}$$

16.
$$\begin{array}{r} 96 \\ \times\,94 \\ \hline \end{array}$$

Find the factors.

1. $X^2 - 16 =$

2. Check #1 by multiplication.

3. $X^2 - 36 =$

4. Check #3 by multiplication.

Find the missing factor.

5. $X - 1 \overline{)\, 2X^2 + 3X + 5}$

6. Check #5 by multiplication.

Find the square root.

7. $\sqrt{4X^2} =$

8. Check #7 by substituting 10 for X, then multiplying to find the product.

Solve using Oriental Squares.

9. $45^2 =$

10. $\begin{array}{r} 3\,7 \\ \times\ 3\,3 \\ \hline \end{array}$

11. Find the factors. $X^2 - 18X + 77.$ 12. Check #11 by multiplication.

13. $(2^5)^5 =$

14. What is the slope of $2Y - 3X + 6 = 0$?

15. What is the point (0, 0) on a graph called?

16. Distribute and fill in the blanks:
    $(D + 2)(X + 3) = D(X + 3) + 2(X + 3) =$ _____+_____+ _____+ _____ .

17. If the federal debt of the U.S. is five trillion dollars, and there are 300 million people, and each person gave $1,000, would that be enough to pay the debt?

18. Solve for X and Y
    using elimination:
    $24Y + 12X = 36$ and $5Y - 5X = 10.$

19. Graph $3Y \leq 2X + 6.$

20. Will the point (–3, –4) satisfy
    the inequality in #19? R $\neq$ 0

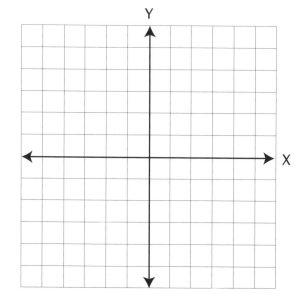

Find the factors.

1. $X^2 - 4 =$

2. Check #1 by multiplication.

3. $X^2 - 25 =$

4. Check #3 by multiplication.

Find the missing factor.

5. $X + 2 \overline{\smash{\big)}\,2X^2 + 7X + 6}$

6. Check #5 by multiplication.

Find the square root.

7. $\sqrt{X^2 + 10X + 25} =$

8. Check #7 by substituting 10 for X, then multiplying to find the product.

Solve using Oriental Squares.

9. $65^2 =$

10.   7 8
    $\times\ 7\ 2$

11. Find the factors of $X^2 + 3X - 4$.   12. Check #11 by multiplication.

13. $(49)^3 = 7^?$ 14. What is the slope of $4Y + 8X + 2 = 0$?

15. Distribute and fill in the blanks:

$(A + B)(C + D + E) = A(\ \ +\ \ +\ \ ) + B(\ \ +\ \ +\ \ ) =$

____ + ____ + ____ + ____ + ____ + ____

16. If the federal debt of the U.S. is five trillion dollars, and there are 300 million people, and each person gave $10,000, would that be enough to pay the debt?

FOR #17–18:

Fill in the table for all the possible whole number options for walking rate and time if the distance is 20 miles.

Rate	Time
20 mph	_____
10 mph	_____
_____	4 hr
4 mph	_____
_____	20 hr

FOR #19–20:

Fill in the table for all the possible whole number options for walking rate and time if the distance is 12 miles.

Rate	Time
12 mph	_____
_____	2 hr
4 mph	_____
3 mph	_____
_____	6 hr
_____	12 hr

Find the factors.

1. $X^2 - 9$

2. Check #1 by multiplication.

3. $X^2 - Y^2$

4. Check #3 by multiplication.

Find the missing factor.

5. $X + 4 \overline{\smash{\big)}\, 2X^3 + 9X^2 + 4X - 8}$

6. Check #5 by multiplication.

Find the square root.

7. $\sqrt{4X^2 + 4X + 1} \ =$

8. Check #7 by substituting 10 for X, then multiplying to find the product.

Solve using Oriental Squares.

9. $85^2 =$

10. $\begin{array}{r} 5\,9 \\ \times\ 5\,1 \\ \hline \end{array}$

11. Find the factors of $X^2 - 10X + 24$. 12. Check #11 by multiplication.

13. Distribute and fill in the blanks:

$(Q + R)(X + Y) = Q(X + Y) + R(X + Y) = $_____ + _____ + _____ + _____

14. If the federal debt of the U.S. is five trillion dollars, and there are 300 million people, how much would each person need to give to pay off the debt?

15. If the federal debt of the U.S. is five trillion dollars, and the interest rate on the loan is 8%, how much interest accumulates each year?

16. Tom Brown drove the 300 miles from Philadelphia to Pittsburgh. He averaged 50 mph. How long did the trip take?

17. How long would it have taken Tom (#16) to travel the 300 miles at a rate of 60 mph?

18. How far will you travel if your speed is 46 mph and your time is 6.5 hours?

19. If you increase your rate by eight mph, how long would it take to travel the same distance as in #18?

20. Solve for X: $4R - 32R = 36R + 8XR$.

The cost of making an item has two parts. The first part is a fixed cost that stays the same no matter how many items are made. This cost reflects expenses, such as those for equipment, rent, and utilities. The second part reflects the actual cost in materials and labor to make one item.

EXAMPLE Our business is making inexpensive paintball guns. The fixed costs for each business vary, but for our example, we are renting a building for $1,500 per month. The price of electricity is $75 per week, and the cost of leasing equipment is $400 per week.

Fixed costs per month:

$1,500 rent
   300 electricity ($75 x 4 weeks)
 1,600 equipment ($400 x 4 weeks)
$3,400 total

If we make only one gun in a month, then the fixed cost per gun is $3,400 plus the cost of labor and materials. If we make 1,000 guns, the fixed costs are only $3.40 per gun. The more guns we can produce per month, the smaller percentage of the cost of each gun will be fixed costs.

The cost for materials for each gun is $4.50. This includes the gun barrel, handle and shooting mechanism. The labor expense is what you pay a person to assemble all of the parts into the finished product. An experienced worker is paid $18 per hour and can assemble one paintball gun in 20 minutes.

Cost of materials and labor for one gun:

$4.50 material
 6.00 labor ($18 x 1/3 hour)
10.50 total

The retail price is what we sell our guns for in our shop at the front of the warehouse. The price of each gun is $30.00. We call this revenue or what comes in as we sell the guns. If we had no fixed costs, our profit would be $30 − 10.50 or $19.50 per gun.

Profit = Revenue − Cost, or P = R − C
$19.50 = 30 − 10.50

Revenue in this case is \$30 x N. (R = 30N) N stands for the number of guns sold in a month. Material and labor cost per gun is \$10.50 x N. However, we know there are also fixed costs of \$3,400 per month, so the total cost per month is (\$10.50 x N) + \$3,400. We can write this as C = 10.50N + 3,400. Read the following equation, or formula, carefully until the numbers make sense.

P = R – C

P = 30N – (10.50N + 3,400) → P = 19.50N – 3,400

If we made and sold 800 paintball guns in one month, did we make a profit?

P = 19.50(800) – 3,400 = \$12,200   Yes, we made \$12,200 profit!

At what point do we break even? In other words, how many guns do we need to produce and sell to pay for all of our costs, some of which are fixed and others of which are materials and labor? To figure this, we'll make the profit equal to zero.

0 = 19.50N – 3,400

3,400 = 19.50N

174.36 = N

We will need to make and sell 175 guns each month to break even. After that we are making a profit.

Answer the questions.

1. If 800 guns are sold in a month for a total profit of \$12,200, what is the profit per gun?

2. What is the total monthly profit if 2,000 guns are sold in a month? Use the information in the example.

3. What is the profit per gun given the sales in number #2?

4. The cost of electricity in our example goes up to $100 per week. Find the new monthly profit for making 800 paintball guns.

A candy manufacturer can produce and sell N boxes of candy in one day. The fixed cost in dollars is 500. The cost of materials and labor for each box is $3. The revenue per box is $5.

5. Write a formula showing the total cost of making a box of candy and another showing the revenue per box.

C =
R =

6. Profit equals revenue minus cost. Write a profit equation for the candy manufacturer.

P =

7. Using your formula, find the profit per box when 500 boxes of candy are sold.

8. Find the profit from selling 2,000 boxes of candy.

9. Find the break-even point for the candy.

Factor completely.

1. $X^4 - 9 =$

2. $X^4 - Y^4 =$

3. $2X^3 - 16X =$

4. $X^8 - Y^4 =$

5. $2X^3 + 10X^2 + 12X =$

6. $5X^3 + 5X^2 - 30X =$

7. $2X^3 + 11X^2 + 5X =$

8. $3X^2 - 12X =$

9. $2X^3 - 18X =$

10. $5X^4 - 20X^3 - 25X^2 =$

11. $4X^3 + 16X^2 - 48X =$

12. $2X^4 - 32 =$

13. $X^3 + 5X^2 + 4X =$

14. $3X^3 + 6X^2 - 9X =$

15. $2X^3 + 7X^2 - 4X =$

16. $4X^3 - 16X =$

Factor completely.

1. $X^4 - 9X^2 =$

2. $3X^3 - 75X =$

3. $4X^4 - 4X^2 =$

4. $5X^5 - 5X =$

5. $-2X^2 - 16X - 30 =$

6. $3X^3 + 9X^2 - 30X =$

7. $5X^3 - 5X^2 - 30X =$

8. $X^3 + 11X^2 + 30X =$

9. $-4X^2 - 28X - 40 =$

10. $-3X^3 - 24X^2 - 36X =$

11. $2X^3 - 8X^2 - 10X =$

12. $5X^5 - X^4 - 6X^3 =$

13. $-3X^3 - 12X^2 + 36X =$

14. $X^4 + 3X^3 - 4X^2 =$

15. $4X^3 - 36X =$

16. $2X^4 - 32X^2 =$

ALGEBRA 1

Find the factors.

1. $X^4 - 16$

2. Check #1 by substituting 10 for X.

3. $16X^2 - 9$

4. Check #3 by substituting 10 for X.

Find the missing factor.

5. $X + 2 \overline{) 3X^2 - 2X - 9}$

6. Check #5 by multiplication.

Build and find the product.

7. $(X - 3)(X - 4) =$

8. Check #7 by multiplying the binomials vertically.

Solve using oriental squares.

9. $75^2 =$

10. $\begin{array}{r} 4\,1 \\ \times\ 4\,9 \\ \hline \end{array}$

11. Find the factors and check: $2X^2 + 4X + 2$.

12. Find the factors and check: $6X^2 - 600$.

Solve for the unknown.

13. $\frac{3}{7} = \frac{6}{Q} = (Q \neq 0)$

14. $\frac{2}{9} = \frac{X}{36}$

15. $.015 = .25Q - .44$

16. $-4X - 16 = -5X + 43$

17. Express 49,703 with exponential notation.

18. Write as a decimal number: $1 \times 10^{-2} + 5 \times 10^{-4}$

19. Find three consecutive integers such that 12 times the second, plus 4 times the first, equals 9 times the third, plus 8.

20. $(2X + 3)(A + 4) = (2X)(\quad + \quad) + (3)(\quad + \quad) = (\quad + \quad) + (\quad + \quad)$

Find the factors.

1. $X^3 - 9X$

2. Check #1 by substituting 10 for X.

3. $X^4 - 81$

4. Check #3 by substituting 10 for X.

Find the missing factor.

5. $X - 3 \overline{\smash{\big)}\ 2X^2 - 7X - 8}$

6. Check #5 by multiplication.

Build and find the product.

7. $(X - 2)(X - 1) =$

8. Check #7 by multiplying the binomials vertically.

Solve using oriental squares.

9. $95^2 =$

10. $\begin{array}{r} 2\ 4 \\ \times\ 2\ 6 \\ \hline \end{array}$

11. Find the factors and check: $5X^2 - 45$.

12. Find the factors and check: $4X^2 - 324$

Solve for the unknown.

13. $\dfrac{4}{11} = \dfrac{P}{110}$

14. $\dfrac{5}{8} = \dfrac{C}{15}$

15. $-50BY + 30B = 80BY - 40B$ $(B \neq 0)$

16. $2.07 - .9X = 5X + .83$

17. Justin has fourteen coins consisting of quarters and dimes. If the total value is $2.30, how many of each kind does he have?

18. If a race car driver travels at 180 mph for 4.2 hours, what is his distance?

19. If the driver in #18 decreases his rate by 30 mph, how long would it take to travel the same distance?

20. $(\ \ + \ \ )(\ \ + \ \ ) = (\ \ )(\ \ + \ \ ) + (\ \ )(\ \ + \ \ ) = (XC + XB) + (AC + AB)$

Find the factors.

1. $X^4 - 25X^2$

2. Check #1 by substituting 10 for X.

3. $5X^3 - 45X$

4. Check #3 by substituting 10 for X.

Find the missing factor.

5. $X + 4 \overline{\smash{\big)}\ 2X^2 + X + 1}$

6. Check #5 by multiplication.

Build and find the product.

7. $(2X - 3)(X - 2) =$

8. Check #7 by multiplying the binomials vertically.

Solve using oriental squares.

9. $25^2 =$

10. $\begin{array}{r} 3\ 2 \\ \times\ 3\ 8 \\ \hline \end{array}$

Solve for the unknown.

11. $\dfrac{12}{72} = \dfrac{A}{8}$

12. $\dfrac{5}{12} = \dfrac{20}{Y}$ $(Y \neq 0)$

13. $-.35Y + .55Y = 2.2$

14. What fraction of 100 is 1?

15. Express .0378 with exponential notation.

16. Write as a decimal number: $2 \times 10^6 + 6 \times 10^4 + 1 \times 10^3$

17. Find three consecutive even integers such that two times the first, plus two times the second, minus five, equals seven plus the third.

18. How many hours will it take to travel 442 miles at 52 mph?

19. If you travel at 212 mph for one hour, how far will you go?

20. $(3X + 2)(X + 3) = ($ $)($ $) + ($ $)($ $) = ($ $+$ $) + ($ $+$ $)$

Here are some more problems involving costs, revenue, and profit.

Answer the questions.

A manufacturer can produce and sell N compact–disc players per week. The per–item cost of producing them is $65 and the fixed costs are $18,000 per week. The total cost in dollars for producing N players can be written as follows: C = $65N + $18,000. Each compact–disc player sells for $100, so revenue for the week can be expressed as R = 100N.

1. Substitute the values for R and C into P = R – C and simplify.

2. Last week 1,000 compact-disc players were sold. What was the profit for the week?

3. What was the per-item profit for the 1,000 compact-disc players in #2?

4. Sales rose until the company was selling 2,000 discs per week. Now what is the weekly profit?

5. At the rate of sales described in #4, what is the profit per item?

6. What is the weekly break-even point for the sale of the compact-disc players?

A clothing manufacturer can produce and sell N cases of socks in one week. The total cost in dollars to produce N cases is $C = 30N + 10,000$. The total revenue is $R = 50N$.

7. Find the profit from selling 1,000 cases of socks. What is the profit per case?

8. Find the profit from selling 2,000 cases of socks. How does the profit per case compare with #7?

9. Find the break-even point for the socks.

Follow the directions. Be sure to factor each equation completely.

For #1-3 $X^2 - 2X - 15 = 0$

1. Find the factors.

2. Find all solutions of X.

3. Check by substituting the solutions.

For #4-6 $X^3 - 3X^2 + 2X = 0$

4. Find the factors.

5. Find all solutions of X.

6. Check by substituting the solutions.

For #7-9 $X^3 - X = 0$

7. Find the factors.

8. Find all solutions of X.

9. Check by substituting the solutions.

For #10-12 $2X^2 - 7X + 3 = 0$

10. Find the factors.

11. Find all solutions of X.

12. Check by substituting the solutions.

Follow the directions. Be sure to factor each equation completely.

For #1-3 $X^2 + X = 56$

1. Find the factors. Make the right side equal to zero first.

2. Find all solutions of X.

3. Check by substituting the solutions.

For #1-3 $X^2 - 11X + 30 = 0$

4. Find the factors.

5. Find all solutions of X.

6. Check by substituting the solutions.

For #7-9 $X^2 - 15X + 56 = 0$

  7. Find the factors.

  8. Find all solutions of X.

  9. Check by substituting the solutions.

For #10-12 $X^2 - 13X + 40 = 0$

10. Find the factors.

11. Find all solutions of X.

12. Check by substituting the solutions.

Find all solutions of X.

1. $2X^2 + 7X + 6 = 0$

2. Check #1 by substituting the solutions.

3. $X^2 + 6X + 8 = 0$

4. Check #3 by substituting the solutions.

5. $X^2 + 3X + 4 = 14$

6. Check #5 by substituting the solutions.

Build and find the product.

7. $(X - 6)(X - 6) =$

8. Check #7 by multiplying the binomials vertically.

9. Use the difference of two squares to find the factors of $X^2 - 16$.

10. Use the difference of two squares to find the factors of $X^2 - 49$.

Simplify.

11. $-4^2 + (-2)^2 =$

12. $3^{-1} \times 3^1 =$

13. $(X^2)^2 (X^{-3})^{-1}$

14. $\dfrac{2X^2X^{-1}Y}{Y^3} - \dfrac{3X^0Y^3}{X^2} + \dfrac{5Y^{-2}}{X^{-1}} =$

(X and Y $\neq$ 0)

15. Rewrite 2X + 4Y – 8 = 0 in slope-intercept form of an equation of a line.

16. What is the slope of a line perpendicular to the line described in #15?

17. What is the GCF of 11 and 33?

18. Find the prime factors of 100.

19. Solve by elimination: Y = X – 3 and Y = 2X – 4.

20. (2X + 3)(2X + 1) = (2X)(⎵ + ⎵) + (⎵)(2X + 1) = (⎵ + ⎵) + (⎵ + ⎵)

Find all solutions of X.

1. $2X^2 + 9X + 4 = 0$

2. Check #1 by substituting the solutions.

3. $X^2 + 13X - 68 = 0$

4. Check #3 by substituting the solutions.

5. $X^2 - 2X + 5 = 8$

6. Check #5 by substituting the solutions.

Build and find the product.

7. $(X - 4)(X - 4) =$

8. Check #7 by multiplying the binomials vertically.

9. Use the difference of two squares to find the factors of $X^2 - Y^2$.

10. Use the difference of two squares to find the factors of $4X^2 - 4Y^2$.

Simplify.

11. $-3^2 - (2)^2 =$

12. $4^{-2} \times 4^3 =$

13. $(X^2)^3 (X^{-2})^2 =$

14. $2B^2B^1 - \dfrac{3B^{-1}}{B^{-4}} + \dfrac{5B^4}{B^{-1}} =$

(when $B \neq 0$)

15. Solve for B: $\dfrac{B}{4} = \dfrac{9}{25}$

16. Solve for R: $\dfrac{3.4}{5} = \dfrac{R}{15}$

17) How long will it take you to travel 520 miles at 65 mph?

18) How fast will you be going if you drive 240 miles in six hours?

19. Solve by substitution: $Y + 2X = -2$ and $X = 4$.

20. $(\quad + \quad)(X + 2) = (3X)(X + 2) + (4)(X + 2) = (\quad + \quad) + (\quad + \quad)$

Find all solutions of X.

1. $4X^2 + 8X + 3 = 0$

2. Check #1 by substituting the solutions.

3. $X^2 + 7X + 12 = 0$

4. Check #3 by substituting the solutions.

5. $X^2 + X + 1 = 13$

6. Check #5 by substituting the solutions.

7. $(X - 5)(X - 5) =$

8. Check #7 by multiplying the binomials vertically.

Build and find the product.

9. Use the difference of two squares to find the factors of $16X^2 - 4$.

10. Use the difference of two squares to find the factors of $X^2 - 100$.

Simplify.

11. $(-3)^2 - (5)^2 =$

12. $2^{-4} \times 2^4 =$

13. $(X^2)^{-3} (X^3)^{-2} =$

14. $5M^4N^2M^{-1} - \dfrac{2NM^4}{N^{-3}M} =$

    (M and N $\neq$ 0)

15. Solve for G: $\dfrac{5}{8} = \dfrac{G}{20}$

16. Solve for T: $\dfrac{7}{2} = \dfrac{100}{T}$

    (T $\neq$ 0)

17. Richard asked his sister to think of a number N and square it, then add two times the number, and subtract two. Write an expression describing his request.

18. If the expression in #17 is equal to 22, what are the value of N?

19. Solve by elimination: $5Y - X = -6$ and $4Y + 3X = -20$.

20. (+)(+) = ( )(+) + ( )(+) = $(3X^2 + X + 6X + 2)$

Not all polynomials can be factored. In fact, there are more non–factorable polynomials than factorable polynomials.

Tell whether each of the following polynomials can be factored, and factor it if possible.

1. $4A^2 + 2$

2. $9A^2 + 4B^2$

3. $2A^2 - 7B^3$

4. $8B^4 + 32B$

5. $2X^2 + 5X + 12$

6. $2X^2 + 7X + 3$

Later on in *Algebra 1*, you will learn how to solve for X in a polynomial that can be factored. In *Algebra 2*, you will learn how to solve polynomials that cannot be factored.

Here are some more exponential equations to graph. These are similar to those in lessons 22 and 23 but involve a negative exponent.

Follow the directions.

7. **Given:** $Y = 3^{-X}$.
    Find the value of Y for each value of X, and fill in the chart.

X	Y
0	
1	
2	
−1	
−2	

8. Plot the points from the chart on the graph and connect them with a curved line.

9. In the graph for #8, what happens to the Y values as the X values get larger? What happens as the X values get smaller?

10. **Given:** $Y = 2^{-X} + 2$.
    Find the value of Y for each value of X, and fill in the chart.

X	Y
0	
1	
2	
3	
-1	
-2	
-3	

11. Plot the points from the chart on the graph and connect them with a curved line.

12. What happens to the Y values as the X values get larger? What happens as the X values get smaller?

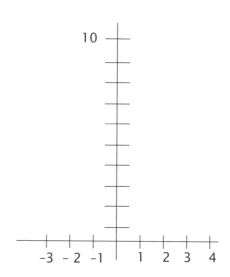

Follow the directions.

For #1-3 84 inches = _____ feet

1. Select the appropriate unit multiplier.

2. Tell which unit of measure goes in the numerator, which goes in the denominator, and why.

3. Solve the equation.

For #4-6 63 feet = _____ yards

4. Select the appropriate unit multiplier.

5. Tell which unit of measure goes in the numerator, which goes in the denominator, and why.

6. Solve the equation.

For #7-9 15 feet = _____ inches

7. Select the appropriate unit multiplier.

8. Tell which unit of measure goes in the numerator, which goes in the denominator, and why.

9. Solve the equation.

For #10-12   25 gallons = _____ quarts

10. Select the appropriate unit multiplier.

11. Tell which unit of measure goes in the numerator, which goes in the denominator, and why.

12. Solve the equation.

For #13-15   272 ounces = _____ pounds

13. Select the appropriate unit multiplier.

14. Tell which unit of measure goes in the numerator, which goes in the denominator, and why.

15. Solve the equation.

For #16-18   52 quarts = _____ gallons

16. Select the appropriate unit multiplier.

17. Tell which unit of measure goes in the numerator, which goes in the denominator, and why.

18. Solve the equation.

Follow the directions. There is a chart of metric measures on the "Symbols and Tables" page.

For #1–3 14 m = _____ cm

1. Select the appropriate unit multiplier.

2. Tell which unit of measure goes in the numerator, which goes in the denominator, and why.

3. Solve the equation.

For #4–6 200 km = _____ m

4. Select the appropriate unit multiplier.

5. Tell which unit of measure goes in the numerator, which goes in the denominator, and why.

6. Solve the equation.

For #7–9 3,500 liters = _____ dkl

7. Select the appropriate unit multiplier.

8. Tell which unit of measure goes in the numerator, which goes in the denominator, and why.

9. Solve the equation.

For #10–12 67,000 ml = _____ liters

10. Select the appropriate unit multiplier.

11. Tell which unit of measure goes in the numerator, which goes in the denominator, and why.

12. Solve the equation.

For #13–15 4.5 hl = _____ liters

13. Select the appropriate unit multiplier.

14. Tell which unit of measure goes in the numerator, which goes in the denominator, and why.

15. Solve the equation.

For #16–18 790 dg = _____ g

16. Select the appropriate unit multiplier.

17. Tell which unit of measure goes in the numerator, which goes in the denominator, and why.

18. Solve the equation.

Follow the directions.

For #1–3 60 inches = _____ feet

1. Select the unit multiplier to be used.

2. Tell which unit of measure goes in the numerator, which goes in the denominator, and why.

3. Solve the equation.

For #4–6 24 feet = _____ yards

4. Select the unit multiplier to be used.

5. Tell which unit of measure goes in the numerator, which goes in the denominator, and why.

6. Solve the equation.

For #7–9 32 ounces = _____ pounds

7. Select the unit multiplier to be used.

8. Tell which unit of measure goes in the numerator, which goes in the denominator, and why.

9. Solve the equation.

For #10–12 28 quarts = _____ gallons

10. Select the unit multiplier to be used.

11. Tell which unit of measure goes in the numerator, which goes in the denominator, and why.

12. Solve the equation.

Follow the directions.

13. $X - 2\sqrt{X^2 - 5X^1 + 10}$

14. Check #13 by multiplication.

15. Find all solutions of X in $3X^2 + 10X + 3 = 0$.

16. Check #15 by substituting the solutions.

17. Find all solutions of X in $.2X^2 - .6X + 1 = 3$.

18. Check #17 by substituting the solutions.

19. Solve for Q: $\dfrac{Q}{.2} = \dfrac{25}{10}$

20. Solve for A: $\dfrac{A}{B} = \dfrac{C}{D}$

Follow the directions.

For #1–3 4 feet = _____ inches

1. Select the unit multiplier to be used.

2. Tell which unit of measure goes in the numerator, which goes in the denominator, and why.

3. Solve the equation.

For #4–6 3 miles = _____ feet

4. Select the unit multiplier to be used.

5. Tell which unit of measure goes in the numerator, which goes in the denominator, and why.

6. Solve the equation.

For #7–9 6 tons = _____ pounds

7. Select the unit multiplier to be used.

8. Tell which unit of measure goes in the numerator, which goes in the denominator, and why.

9. Solve the equation.

For #10–12 2 1/2 quarts = _____ pints

10. Select the unit multiplier to be used.

11. Tell which unit of measure goes in the numerator, which goes in the denominator, and why.

12. Solve the equation.

Follow the directions.

13. Find all solutions of X in
$2X^2 - 3X - 5 = 0$.

14. Check #13 by substituting
the solutions.

15. Find all solutions of X in
$3X^2 + 8X + 4 = 0$.

16. Check #15 by substituting
the solutions.

17. Find all solutions of Y in
$3Y^2 - 12 = 0$.

18. Check #17 by substituting
the solutions.

QUICK TIP

Distance equals rate times time.

EXAMPLE 1   What is your distance if you travel at 53 mph for four hours?

This can be written as D = RT. Think of unit multipliers for help in understanding this equation.

$$\frac{X \text{ miles}}{1} = \frac{53 \text{ miles}}{1 \text{ hour}} \times \frac{4 \text{ hours}}{1} \rightarrow X = 212 \text{ miles}$$

19. What is your distance if you travel at 65 mph for three hours?

20. What is your distance if you travel at 45 mph for five hours?

Answer the questions.

For #1–3 7,920 feet = _____ inches

   1. Select the unit multiplier to be used.

   2. Tell which unit of measure goes in the numerator, which goes in the denominator, and why.

   3. Solve the equation.

For #4–6 10,000 pounds = _____ tons

   4. Select the unit multiplier to be used.

   5. Tell which unit of measure goes in the numerator, which goes in the denominator, and why.

   6. Solve the equation.

For #7–9 5 pounds = _____ ounces

   7. Select the unit multiplier to be used.

   8. Tell which unit of measure goes in the numerator, which goes in the denominator, and why.

   9. Solve the equation.

For #10–12 13 quarts = _____ pints

   10. Select the unit multiplier to be used.

   11. Tell which unit of measure goes in the numerator, which goes in the denominator, and why.

   12. Solve the equation.

Follow the directions.

13. Find all solutions of X in
    $2X^2 + X - 6 = 0$.

14. Check #13 by substituting
    the solutions.

15. Find all solutions of B in
    $5B^2 - 125 = 0$.

16. Check #15 by substituting
    the solutions.

17. Find all solutions of X in
    $6X^2 - 6X + 18 = 90$.

18. Check #17 by substituting
    the solutions.

QUICK TIP

More on distance problems.

D = RT can also be written as R = D/T

(rate equals distance divided by time).

EXAMPLE 1   What is your rate if you travel 100 miles in two hours?

$$\frac{X \text{ miles}}{1 \text{ hour}} = \frac{100 \text{ miles}}{2 \text{ hours}} \quad \rightarrow \quad \text{rate} = \frac{50 \text{ miles}}{1 \text{ hour}}, \text{ or 50 mph.}$$

19. Joe Tribble ran six miles in 30 minutes. What is his rate in
    miles per hour? (Hint: first change his time to hours.)

20. Prefontaine ran 10 miles in 48 minutes. What is
    his rate in miles per hour?

Factoring four terms at a time requires the use of the associative and distributive properties.

EXAMPLE

Factor $Y^3 - Y^2 + 3Y - 3$

$(Y^3 - Y^2) + (3Y - 3)$ Group in pairs that have a common factor.

$Y^2(Y - 1) + 3(Y - 1)$ Factor each set separately.

$(Y - 1)(Y^2 + 3)$ We can use the distributive property in reverse because each part of the equation has a $(Y - 1)$ factor.

The polynomials below have been carefully chosen to give you practice in factoring. Remember that in real life, not all polynomials can be factored.

Factor each polynomial. If necessary, use the associative property to change the order of the terms before grouping them.

1. $2X^3 - X^2 + 4X - 2$

2. $3A^3 - 6A^2 - A + 2$

3. $2B^3 + 3B^2 + 2B + 3$

4. $2X^4 + 4X^3 - 3X - 6$

5. $4Y^2 + 6Y - 2Y - 3$

6. $6P^4 - 6P^3 + 14P^2 - 14P$

Complex problems with polynomials can often be simplified by using factoring.

EXAMPLE

$$\frac{X^2 - 4X + 4}{X^2 - X - 12} \cdot \frac{X^2 + X - 20}{X^2 + X - 6} =$$

$$\frac{(X-2)(X-2)}{(X-4)(X+3)} \cdot \frac{(X-4)(X+5)}{(X-2)(X+3)} = \frac{(X-2)\cancel{(X-2)}}{\cancel{(X-4)}(X+3)} \cdot \frac{\cancel{(X-4)}(X+5)}{\cancel{(X-2)}(X+3)}$$

Factor each polynomial, and then cancel like terms.

$$\frac{(X-2)(X+5)}{(X+3)(X+3)} = \frac{X^2 + 3X - 10}{X^2 + 6X + 9}$$

Write the remaining factors and multiply them.

Use factoring to help you multiply or divide. Remember to invert and multiply when dividing fractions.

7. $\dfrac{X^3 + X^2 - 2X}{X^2 + 2X - 3} \cdot \dfrac{X + 3}{X^2 + 2X} =$

8. $\dfrac{X + 5}{X^2 + 3X + 2} \div \dfrac{X^2 - 3X}{X^3 - X^2 - 6X} =$

Use unit multipliers to solve.

1. 1 ft^2 (square foot) = _____ in^2 (square inches)

2. 2 ft^2 (square feet) = _____ in^2 (square inches)

3. 1 yd^2 (square yard) = _____ ft^2 (square feet)

4. 1 yd^3 (cubic yard) = _____ in^3 (cubic inches)

5. 2 ft^3 (cubic feet) = _____ in^3 (cubic inches)

6. 8 cm^2 (square centimeters) = _____ mm^2 (square millimeters)

7. 9 yd^2 (square yards) = _____ in^2 (square inches)

8. 1 mi^2 (square mile) = _____ ft^2 (square feet)

9. 100 ft^2 (square feet) = _____ yd^2 (square yards)

10. $.5 \text{ yd}^2$ (square yards) = _____ ft^2 (square feet)

11. 300 ft^2 (square feet) = _____ mi^2 (square miles)

12. 950 cm^2 (square centimeters) = _____ m^2 (square meters)

Fill in the blanks.

13. 1 acre = _____ ft^2 (square feet)

14. 1 cord (of wood) = _____ ft x _____ ft x_____ ft = _____ ft^3 (cubic feet)

15. 1 yard (of concrete) = _____ ft^3 (cubic feet)

16. 1 yard (of carpet) = _____ ft^2 (square feet)

Use unit multipliers to solve.

1. 7 ft^2 (square feet) = _____ in^2 (square inches)

2. 3 m^2 (square meters) = _____ cm^2 (square centimeters)

3. .8 ft^2 (square feet) = _____ in^2 (square inches)

4. 1.5 ft^2 (square feet) = _____ in^2 (square inches)

5. 8 m^3 (cubic meters) = _____ dm^3 (cubic decimeters)

6. 3 km^3 (cubic kilometers) = _____ m^3 (cubic meters)

7. 5.6 ft^3 (cubic feet) = _____ in^3 (cubic inches)

8. 2 ft^3 (cubic feet) = _____ in^3 (cubic inches)

9. 7 yd^3 (cubic yards) = _____ in^3 (cubic inches)

10. 4 mi^3 (cubic miles) = _____ in^3 (cubic inches) You may round the answer.

11. 370 cm^3 (cubic centimeters) = _____ m^3 (cubic meters)

12. 18 cm^2 (square centimeters) = _____ m^2 (square meters)

Fill in the blanks.

13. 2 acres = _____ ft^2 (square feet)

14. 1 cord (of wood) = _____ ft x _____ ft x _____ ft = _____ ft^3 (cubic feet)

15. 2 yards (of concrete) = _____ ft^3 (cubic feet)

16. 2 yards (of carpet) = _____ ft^2 (square feet)

Use unit multipliers to solve.

1. $1 \text{ ft}^2 = $ _____ in^2

2. $1 \text{ yd}^2 = $ _____ ft^2

3. $1 \text{ mi}^2 = $ _____ ft^2

4. $1 \text{ m}^2 = $ _____ cm^2

5. $4 \text{ ft}^2 = $ _____ in^2

6. $7 \text{ yd}^2 = $ _____ ft^2

7. $3.2 \text{ mi}^2 = $ _____ ft^2

8. $15.7 \text{ m}^2 = $ _____ cm^2

9. 1 acre = _____ ft^2

10. 1 yard (of carpet) = _____ ft^2

Follow the directions.

11. Find all solutions of X.

$3X^2 - 5X + 2 = 0$

12. Check #11 by substituting the solutions.

13. Find all solutions of X.

$2X^2 - 10X + 12 = 0$

14. Check #13 by substituting the solutions.

15. $(X - 4)^2 =$

16. $35^2 \bigcirc 32 \times 38$ (<, >, or =)

17. Build a rectangle and find the factors. $X^2 + 7X + 10 = ($ + $)($ + $)$

18. Build and write the product. $(3X + 2)(X + 2)$

19. What percent of a yard is a foot?

20. What fraction of a square yard is a square foot?

Use unit multipliers to solve.

1. $9 \text{ ft}^2 = $ _____ in^2

2. $5 \text{ yd}^2 = $ _____ ft^2

3. $6 \text{ mi}^2 = $ _____ ft^2

4. $18 \text{ m}^2 = $ _____ cm^2

5. $.75 \text{ ft}^2 = $ _____ in^2

6. $1.3 \text{ yd}^2 = $ _____ ft^2

7. $25 \text{ mi}^2 = $ _____ ft^2

8. $.67 \text{ m}^2 = $ _____ cm^2

9. 5 acres = _____ ft^2

10. 2 cords of wood = _____ ft^3

Follow the directions.

11. Find all solutions of X. $3X^2 - 9X - 12 = 0$

12. Check #11 by substituting the solutions.

13. Find all solutions of X. $X^2 - 36 = 0$

14. Check #13 by substituting the solutions.

15. $(X - 5)^2 =$ 16. $45^2 \bigcirc 40 \times 50$ (<, >, or =)

17. Build a rectangle and find the factors.
    $X^2 + 10X + 21 = ($ + $)($ + $)$

18. Build and write the product. $(X + 3)(X - 9)$

19. What percent of a yard is an inch?

20. What fraction of a square foot is a square inch?

Use unit multipliers to solve.

1. $27 \text{ ft}^2 = $ _____ yd^2

2. $3 \text{ yd}^2 = $ _____ ft^2

3. $10,000 \text{ ft}^2 = $ _____ mi^2

4. $1,200 \text{ cm}^2 = $ _____ m^2

5. $1 \text{ ft}^3 = $ _____ in^3

6. $1 \text{ yd}^3 = $ _____ ft^3

7. $1 \text{ mi}^3 = $ _____ ft^3 You may round the answer.

8. $3 \text{ m}^3 = $ _____ cm^3

9. 3 cords of wood $= $ _____ ft^3

10. 2 yards (of concrete) = _____ ft^3

Follow the directions.

11. Find all solutions of X. $X^2 - 10X + 25 = 0$

12. Check #11 by substituting the solutions.

13. Find all solutions of X. $X^2 - 12X + 35 = 0$

14. Check #13 by substituting the solutions.

15. $(3X - 1)(X - 2) =$ 16. 73 x 77 $\bigcirc$ 60 x 80   (<, >, or =)

17. What percent of a square yard is a square foot?

18. What fraction of a square mile is an acre?

19. Carl Lewis ran 100 yards in nine seconds. What is his rate in yards per second?

20. Cameron traveled 200 miles in five hours. What is his rate in miles per hour?

Here are some application problems that involve polynomial factoring. You will learn more about this kind of problem if you take physics. Be sure to check each answer for reasonableness.

EXAMPLE   An object is thrown down from the top of a building 320 feet high at an initial, or starting, speed of 16 feet per second. How many seconds later will the object reach the ground?

Use this equation: $d = vt + 16t^2$

where d = distance in feet
      v = initial speed in ft/sec (velocity)
      t = time in seconds

$d = vt + 16 t^2$
$320 = 16 t + 16 t^2$
$16 t^2 + 16t - 320 = 0$
$16(t^2 + t - 20) = 0$
$16(t - 4)(t + 5) = 0$
$t = 4, t = -5$

In this case, negative five seconds makes no sense, so the object will take four seconds to reach the ground.

Solve. Remember to check each solution to see whether it is a valid, real–life answer.

1.   A similar object is thrown down from the top of a building 96 feet high at the same initial speed of 16 feet per second. How many seconds will it take the object to reach the ground this time?

2. Carl dropped a rock with an initial speed of eight feet per second into a well from three feet above the well. It is 77 feet from the top of the well to the surface of the water. How many seconds later will Carl hear the splash?

   (Do not worry about the speed of sound.)

3. A helicopter was hovering 2,000 feet above the ground. An object was thrown downward from the helicopter and hit the top of an 80-foot-tall building. If the initial speed of the object was 32 feet per second, how many seconds did it take for the object to hit the building?

This problem uses the same equation to find distance instead of time.

4. Jeff stood on the top of a tower and threw down an object with an initial speed of 10 feet per second. The object reached the ground four seconds later. How high is the tower?

Fill in the blanks with approximate values.

1. 1 inch = _____ centimeters

2. 1 yard = _____ meters

3. 1 mile = _____ kilometers

4. 1 ounce = _____ grams

Use unit multipliers to make the following conversions.

5. 10 kilometers = _____ miles

6. 45 ounces = _____ grams

7. 21 kilograms = _____ pounds

8. 15 yards = _____ meters

Use unit multipliers to make the following conversions.

9. 15 centimeters = _____ inches

10. 25 grams = _____ ounces

11. 5 quarts = _____ liters

12. 54 inches = _____ centimeters

13. 5 kilometers = _____ miles

14. 45 pounds = _____ kilograms

15. 105 ounces = _____ grams

16. 63 yards = _____ meters

Fill in the blanks with approximate values.

1. 1 centimeter = _____ inches

2. 1 meter = _____ yards

3. 1 kilogram = _____ pounds

4. 1 liter = _____ quarts

Use unit multipliers to make the following conversions.

5. 25 centimeters = _____ inches

6. 36 grams = _____ ounces

7. 12 quarts = _____ liters

8. 110 inches = _____ centimeters

Use unit multipliers to make the following conversions.

9. 36 inches = _____ centimeters

10. 75.5 grams = _____ ounces

11. 18.5 yards = _____ meters

12. 55 kilograms = _____ pounds

13. 16.3 miles = _____ kilometers

14. 36 liters = _____ quarts

15. 5.05 ounces = _____ grams

16. 360.5 centimeters = _____ inches

Convert from imperial to metric measures.

1. 5 inches = _____ cm

2. 3 quarts = _____ liters

3. 10 ounces = _____ grams

4. 62 pounds = _____ kilograms

Find the missing factor.

5. $2X + 1\overline{)6X^3 + 5X^2 + 9X + 1}$

6. Check #5 by multiplication.

7. $\sqrt{9X^4}$ =
    (X is positive)

8. Check #7 by substituting 10 for X, then multiplying to find the product.

9. 3.5 acres = _____ square feet

10. 1 square mile = _____ square feet

11. 13 x 17 $\bigcirc$ 16 x 14

12. 5 yd^2 $\bigcirc$ 50 ft^2

13. $(X + 6)^2$ =

14. What is the slope of a line parallel to X − 2Y = 4 ?

15. Find all possible solutions for $X^2 + 5X + 6 = 20$.

16. Check your answers for #15.

17. (+   )(+   ) = (2X)(X + 2) + (3)(X + 2) = (+   +   +   )

18. When Katie started her business, she owed $100. After that, she earned $400 a week. Write an equation showing the growth of her earnings. Graph the equation, letting each space on the graph stand for $100.

19. Using the graph, tell what Katie's assets will be after one week.

20. Using the equation, tell what Katie's assets will be after 30 weeks.

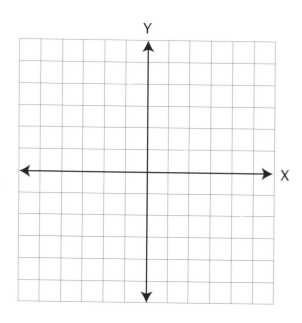

Convert from imperial to metric measures.

1. 7 mi = _____ km

2. 8 lb (pounds) = _____ kg

3. 4 yd = _____ m

4. 2 qt (quarts) = _____ liters

Find the missing factor.

5. $X - 2 \overline{\smash{\big)}\ 2X^3 - 9X^2 - 4X + 7}$

6. Check #5 by multiplication.

7. $\sqrt{16X^2}$ =
    (X is positive)

8. $\sqrt{Y^2X^4}$ =
    (X and Y are positive)

9. 100,000 square feet = _____ acres

10. 1.34 square meters = _____ square centimeters

11. 82 x 88 ◯ 86 x 84

12. 7 yd^3 ◯ 175 ft^3

13. $(X - 3)^2 =$

14. What is the slope of of a
    line perpendicular to X − 2Y = 4?

15. Find all possible solutions for $X^2 - 12X + 35 = 15$.

16. Check your answers for #15.

17. $(2X + 7)(\quad + \quad) = (\quad)(X + 2) + (\quad)(X + 2) = (\quad + \quad + \quad + \quad)$

18. If distance equals rate times time, or D = RT, then T = _____ .

19. Ethan ran 12 miles at 6 mph. How long did it take him?

20. Graph 2Y < 3X − 2.

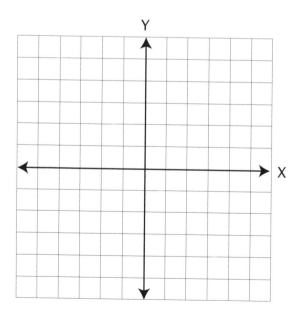

Convert from metric to imperial measures.

1. 25 km = _____ miles

2. 7 m = _____ yards

3. 11 kg = _____ lb

4. 10 liters = _____ qt

Find the missing factor.

(In number 5, there is no X^2 term in the polynomial to be divided. Before dividing, you must rewrite the polynomial as $4X^3 + 0X^2 + X - 3$. Use this procedure when dividing any polynomial with a missing term.)

5. $2X - 3 \overline{)\, 4X^3 + 7X - 3}$

6. Check #5 by multiplication.

7. $\sqrt{144} =$

8. $\sqrt{25X^6} =$

9. 1.75 yd of carpet = _____ ft^2

10. How many yards of carpet are needed for a room 25' x 18'? (You cannot buy a part of a yard.)

11. 13 x 17 $\bigcirc$ 16 x 14

12. 5 yd^2 $\bigcirc$ 50 ft^2

13. $(X - 2)^2 =$

14. $(X + 4)^2 =$

15. Find all possible solutions for $X^2 + 7X - 18 = 42$.

16. Check your answers for #15.

17. Joseph jogged 4 miles at 6 mph. How long did he jog?

18. Sandi walked 4 miles at 3 mph. How long did she walk?

19. Peter had P pennies. Drew had two times as many pennies as Peter had. Drew lost two pennies and found seven. Peter gave him his pennies, which Drew promptly lost. Write an expression in terms of P showing Drew's experience.

20. If Drew now has 11 pennies, how many did Peter have to start with (the value of P)?

Traditional measuring systems used everyday objects and dimensions of the human body as standards.

Here are some examples.

Inch	Width of a thumb
Foot	Length of a human foot
Yard	The length from the tip of the nose to the end of the fingers of an outstretched arm
Cubit	Length of the forearm; 18 inches
Rod	Twenty feet; used in measuring land
Furlong	Length of a furrow plowed by an ox
Acre	Area of an Anglo-Saxon field that could be plowed in one morning using oxen
Pace	Two steps of a soldier; approximately five feet
Mile	Length of 1,000 paces of a Roman legion

Use the information given to answer the questions.

1. The ark described in Genesis was 300 cubits long. How many feet is that?

2. The Genesis ark (#2) was 50 cubits wide and 30 cubits high. What was the volume of the ark in cubic feet?

3. How many feet long was the Roman mile? How does that compare with the length of the modern mile?

4. Find the number of square feet in a modern mile, and round to the nearest million. Assuming a modern acre is about the same as an Anglo-Saxon acre, how many mornings would a team of oxen have to work to plow a square mile of land?

5. When a seamstress holds a length of fabric in her two hands with one arm outstretched and the other with her hand in front of her face, what unit of measure is she finding?

6. Chris measured his own foot and found it was 10 inches long. He measured the length of a room by stepping heel to toe and got 18 "Chris feet." He concluded that the room was somewhat less than 18 feet long. What was the length of the room in standard feet?

7. It is convenient to carry your own quick-measuring tools about with you. Measure your own foot and thumb, and see how they compare to standard measures. Then use these handy tools to estimate the size of objects. Don't forget to re-measure later if you are still growing!

Simplify. All variables in this lesson will be assumed to be positive.

1. $16^{\frac{3}{2}} =$

2. $2^{\frac{2}{1}} =$

3. $100^{\frac{1}{2}} =$

4. $8^{\frac{2}{3}} =$

5. $(X^{\frac{5}{1}})^{\frac{1}{10}} =$

6. $(Y^{\frac{1}{3}})^{\frac{1}{5}} =$

7. $(Y^3 \times Y^5)^{\frac{1}{4}} =$

8. $16^{\frac{3}{4}} =$

9. $(27^{\frac{1}{3}})^{\frac{4}{1}} =$

10. $8^{\frac{1}{3}} \cdot 16 =$

11. $(64^{\frac{1}{2}})^{\frac{2}{3}} =$

12. $(X^5 \cdot X^7)^{\frac{1}{2}} =$

13. $(M^{\frac{1}{2}} \cdot M^{\frac{2}{3}})^{\frac{6}{1}} =$

14. $[(X^3)^5 \cdot X^5]^{\frac{1}{2}} =$

15. $[(X^5)^{\frac{2}{3}}]^{\frac{1}{6}} =$

16. $[(M^8)^{\frac{1}{2}}]^{\frac{3}{4}} =$

Simplify. All variables in this lesson will be assumed to be positive.

1. $32^{\frac{2}{5}} =$

2. $9^{\frac{3}{1}} =$

3. $81^{\frac{1}{2}} =$

4. $625^{\frac{3}{4}} =$

5. $(X^6)^{\frac{1}{3}} =$

6. $(Y^{\frac{1}{2}})^{\frac{1}{7}} =$

7. $(Y^4 \cdot Y^6)^{\frac{1}{5}} =$

8. $27^{\frac{2}{3}} =$

9. $(81^{\frac{1}{4}})^{\frac{5}{1}} =$

10. $64^{\frac{1}{3}} \cdot 64^{\frac{1}{3}} =$

11. $(16^{\frac{1}{3}})^{\frac{3}{4}} =$

12. $(X^3 \cdot X^5)^{\frac{1}{4}} =$

13. $(Y^{\frac{1}{2}} \cdot Y^{\frac{3}{4}})^{\frac{4}{1}} =$

14. $[(X^3)^{\frac{1}{3}} \cdot X^4]^{\frac{1}{5}} =$

15. $[(X^4)^{\frac{3}{5}}]^{\frac{1}{6}} =$

16. $(Y^6 \cdot Y^8)^{\frac{1}{2}} =$

Simplify.

1. $8^{\frac{1}{3}} =$

2. $9^{\frac{1}{2}} =$

3. $5^{\frac{3}{1}} =$

4. $1{,}000^{\frac{2}{3}} =$

5. $(X^2)^{\frac{3}{2}} =$

6. $2^{\frac{1}{3}} \cdot 4 =$

7. $(Y^{\frac{2}{3}})(Y^{\frac{1}{4}}) =$

8. $(5^{\frac{1}{4}})(5^{\frac{2}{3}}) =$

Follow the directions.

9. 8 in = _____ cm

10. 30 qt = _____ liters

11. 72 x 78 $\bigcirc$ (75)(75)

12. 2 mi^2 $\bigcirc$ 1,200 acres

13. $(A + B)^2 =$

14. $(X - 2)(X^2 + 2X + Y^2) =$

15. Find the factors: $X^2 + 11X + 24$.

16. Solve for X and Y using substitution: $5Y + 3X = 10$ and $-4Y - 4X = 20$.

17. Look up how many square miles there are in your state, and then change the square miles to square feet. (Look at your answer to lesson practice 29C, #3, to find the number of square feet in one square mile.)

18. If there are six billion people in the world, how many square feet would each person receive if everyone was invited to your state?

19. A swimming pool with a diameter of 12 feet and a height of 4 feet contains about 452 cubic feet of water. Since a cubic foot of water weighs 62 pounds, what does the water in the pool weigh?

20. What does the water in #19 weigh in tons (to the nearest ton)?

Simplify.

1. $4^{\frac{3}{2}} =$

2. $81^{\frac{1}{2}} =$

3. $7^{\frac{2}{1}} =$

4. $64^{\frac{1}{3}} =$

5. $(Y^{\frac{3}{2}})^{\frac{1}{2}} =$

6. $10^{\frac{1}{3}} \cdot 1{,}000 =$

7. $(A^{\frac{3}{4}})(A^{\frac{1}{4}}) =$

8. $(X^2)^{\frac{3}{4}} =$

Follow the directions.

9. 50 mi = _____ km

10. 100 oz = _____ g

11. 43 x 47 $\bigcirc$ (45)(45)

12. .25 acres $\bigcirc$ 12,000 ft^2

13. $(X - A)^2 =$

14. $(X + 2)(X^2 - 2X + 4) =$

15. Find the product, or area, of $(X - 1)(X - 6)$.

16. Solve for X and Y using substitution: $Y - X = 0$ and $X = -4$.

17. Look up how many square miles there are in Texas, and then change the square miles to square feet.

18. If there are six billion people in the world, how many square feet would each person receive if everyone was invited to live in Texas?

19. A swimming pool with a diameter of 15 feet and a height of 4 feet contains about 706 cubic feet of water. Since a cubic foot of water weighs 62 pounds, what does the water in the pool weigh?

20. What does the water in #19 weigh in tons (to the nearest ton)?

Simplify.

1. $10^{\frac{4}{1}} =$

2. $25^{\frac{3}{2}} =$

3. $13^{\frac{4}{4}} =$

4. $16^{\frac{3}{2}} =$

5. $(A^3)^{\frac{1}{3}} =$

6. $3^{\frac{1}{2}} \cdot 27 =$

7. $(X^{\frac{5}{6}})(X^{\frac{1}{2}}) =$

8. $(2^{\frac{1}{3}})(2^{\frac{1}{2}})(2^{\frac{7}{6}}) =$

Follow the directions.

9. 10 m = _____ yd

10. 20 kg = _____ lb

11. 2 cubic feet = _____ cubic inches

12. 14 cubic yards = _____ cubic feet

13. $(5A + 5B)^2 =$

14. $(X - Y)(X^2 + XY + Y^2) =$

15. Find the product, or area, of $(X + 1)(4X + 6)$.

16. Solve for X and Y using elimination: $3Y - 4X = 2$ and $6 + Y = 2X$.

17. Look up how many square miles there are in Alaska, and then change the square miles to square feet.

18. If there are six billion people in the world, how many square feet would each person receive if everyone lived in Alaska?

19. How many cubic feet of water would cover an area 100 ft by 100 ft to a depth of 50 ft? (Remember to multiply length by width by depth of the water to find the volume.) Since a cubic foot of water weighs 62 pounds, what does the water weigh?

20. What does the water in #19 weigh in tons (to the nearest ton)?

Here are some measurement equivalents traditionally used in English–speaking countries.

4 rods = 1 chain	8 furlongs = 1 mile
22 yards = 1 chain	3 miles = 1 league
10 chains = 1 furlong (about the length of a Roman stadium)	

Use the information given to answer the questions.

1. How far did Captain Nemo's submarine travel in furlongs, if it traveled 20,000 leagues under the sea?

2. If a farmer owned a farm that had a width of 1,920 rods, how many miles wide was it?

3. How many rods are in one furlong?

4. Show that there are 5,280 feet in a mile, using unit multipliers and the English conversions above.

The basic unit of weight in the English system was the grain. It was based on the weight of a grain of barley.

7,000 grains = 1 pound	20 hundredweight = 1 ton
14 pounds = 1 stone	8 pounds = 1 gallon
2 stones = 1 quarter	2 gallons = 1 peck
4 quarters = 1 hundredweight	4 pecks = 1 bushel

5. How many pounds are in a ton in this measuring system? How does that compare with our American ton?

6. Originally, a gallon of wheat in the English system was eight pounds of wheat. How many bushels would be equal to 6,400 pounds of wheat?

7. How many English tons would you have if you had 6,400 pounds of wheat?

8. How many pounds of apples would you expect in a one-half bushel basket?

Write each number using scientific notation.

1. 500,000 =

2. 356,000,000 =

3. 54,800,000 =

4. .00096 =

5. .00468 =

6. .0000000913 =

Use scientific notation to solve. Follow the steps given.

Step 1 Estimate your answer by rounding each number to one significant digit before multiplying or dividing.
Step 2 Rewrite each factor using scientific notation.
Step 3 Multiply or divide the numbers and the exponents separately.
Step 4 Make sure your final answer is in correct form.
Step 5 Check for significant digits.
Step 6 Check your answer using a calculator.

7. 190,000 x 6,000,000 =

8. 181,500 x 4,160,000,000 =

9. 860,000 x 36,400,000 =

10. .000085 x 9,000,000,000 =

11. .00093 x 50,000 =

12. .0021 x .000350 =

13. 560,000 ÷ 4,000,000,000 =

14. $\dfrac{9,800,000}{2,450,000}$ =

15. .0036 ÷ .012 =

Write each number using scientific notation.

1. 600,000 =

2. 854,000,000 =

3. 62,800,000 =

4. .000095 =

5. .00528 =

6. .000000921 =

Use scientific notation to solve. Follow the steps given.

Step 1 Estimate your answer by rounding each number to one significant digit before multiplying or dividing.
Step 2 Rewrite each factor using scientific notation.
Step 3 Multiply or divide the numbers and the exponents separately.
Step 4 Make sure your final answer is in correct form.
Step 5 Check for significant digits.
Step 6 Check your answer using a calculator.

7. 180,000 x 5,000,000 =

8. 915,000 x 3,000,000 =

9. 96,000 x 43,600,000 =

10. .000075 x 9,000,000,000 =

11. .000079 x 62,500 =

12. .00031 x .0000004 =

13. 52,000 ÷ 40,000,000 =

14. $\dfrac{24,000,000}{60,000,000,000}$ =

15. .00035 ÷ .007 =

Write each number in scientific notation.

1. 700,000 =

2. .0076 =

For #3-6   5,000 x 8,000,000 =

3. Estimate your answer and rewrite each number using scientific notation.

4. Multiply the numbers and the exponents.

5. Simplify and check for significant digits.

6. Check your answer using a calculator.

For #7-10   61,300 ÷ 120 =

7. Estimate your answer and rewrite each number using scientific notation.

8. Divide the numbers and the exponents.

9. Simplify and check for significant digits.

10. Check your answer using a calculator.

Solve.

11. $1{,}000^{\frac{2}{3}} \cdot 10^{2} \cdot 10^{-3} =$

12. $8^{\frac{2}{3}} \cdot 4 =$

13. $10^{\frac{1}{3}} \cdot 100^{\frac{3}{2}} \cdot 10^{-1} =$

14. $A^{5} A^{\frac{-1}{2}} A^{\frac{-3}{2}} =$

15. $10 \text{ km} = \underline{\hspace{2cm}} \text{ miles}$

16. $75 \text{ grams} = \underline{\hspace{2cm}} \text{ ounces}$

17. $(3X - 3Y)^{2} =$

18. $(X + Y)(X^{2} - XY + Y^{2}) =$

Find all solutions for X and check.

19. $X(X + 4) + 5X + 3 = -17$

20. $X(2X - 9) = 0$

Write each number in scientific notation.

1. 586,000,000 =

2. .000595 =

For #3-6   18,000 x .0072 =

3. Estimate your answer and rewrite each number using scientific notation.

4. Multiply the numbers and the exponents.

5. Simplify and check for significant digits.

6. Check your answer using a calculator.

For #7-10   1,450,000 ÷ 290 =

7. Estimate your answer and rewrite each number using scientific notation.

8. Divide the numbers and the exponents.

9. Simplify and check for significant digits.

10. Check your answer using a calculator.

Solve.

11. $(5^{\frac{1}{2}})^{-4} 5^0 5^2 =$

12. $9^{\frac{3}{2}} \cdot 27 \cdot 81^{\frac{1}{4}} =$

13. 26 miles = _____ km

14. 500 grams = _____ ounces

15. $(D - 5)(D^2 + 5D + 25) =$

16. $(A + T)(\text{\_\_\_\_} - \text{\_\_\_\_} + \text{\_\_\_\_}) = A^3 + T^3$

Try setting this up like a long division problem.

Find all solutions for X and check.

17. $X(5X - 10) = 0$

18. $X^2 + 7X - 18 = 42$

19. Find three consecutive odd integers such that ten times the first, plus two times the second, minus four times the third, plus eight, equals three times the third, minus eleven.

20. Nicole has 16 coins consisting of dimes and nickels. If she has a total of $1.35, how many of each coin does she have?

Write each number in scientific notation.

1. 23,800,000 =

2. .000000112 =

For #3-6   .92 x 640,000 =

3. Estimate your answer and rewrite each number using scientific notation.

4. Multiply the numbers and the exponents.

5. Simplify and check for significant digits.

6. Check your answer using a calculator.

For #7-10   .4 x .25 ÷ .001 =

7. Estimate your answer and rewrite each number using scientific notation.

8. Multiply and divide the numbers and the exponents.

9. Simplify and check for significant digits.

10. Check your answer using a calculator.

Solve.

11. $A^{\frac{3}{4}} A^{\frac{4}{3}} =$

12. $9^{\frac{1}{2}} \cdot 3^2 \cdot 27^{\frac{4}{3}} =$

13. $100 \text{ m} = \underline{\hspace{2cm}} \text{ yd}$

14. $2 \text{ liters} = \underline{\hspace{2cm}} \text{ qt}$

15. Factor: $X^2 - B^2$

16. Factor: $4X^5 - 324X$

Find all possible solutions and check.

17. $X^2 + X - 12 = 60$

18. $4 - A^2 = 0$

Use scientific notation to solve the problems.

19. Look up how many square miles there are in North America. Change square miles to square feet.

20. If there are six billion people in the world, how many square feet would each person receive if everyone lived in North America? What fraction or decimal part of an acre is that? Round the number of square feet in an acre to 44,000 for this and similar problems.

In chemistry, formulas for compounds are studied. A familiar compound is H_2O (water). Another familiar one is H_2O_2 (hydrogen peroxide). The small numbers that extend below the line of print are called subscripts. In the first formula above, the letters and subscript tell us that one molecule of water has two atoms of hydrogen and one atom of oxygen. Hydrogen peroxide has two atoms of hydrogen and two atoms of oxygen in each molecule.

The mass of one molecule of a compound (molecular mass) is computed by taking the weights for each element from a chart called the periodic table and multiplying by the number of atoms of that element in the molecule. Molecular mass is measured in very small units called atomic mass units (amu).

EXAMPLE 1 Hydrogen has a weight of 1.008 amu, and oxygen has a weight of 16.00 amu. What is the molecular mass of hydrogen peroxide? (H_2O_2)

2(1.008) amu + 2(16.00) amu = 34.016 amu

Since this is a measure of weight or mass, use the idea of significant digits to round your answer to 34.02 amu.

Here are the atomic weights needed to complete this lesson.

C	carbon	12.0 amu	Na	sodium	22.0 amu
Cl	chlorine	35.5 amu	O	Oxygen	16.00 amu
H	hydrogen	1.008 amu			

Find the mass in amu. Use significant digits as needed to round your answers.

1. What is the mass of one water molecule?

2. What is the mass of one molecule of $NaHCO_3$ (baking soda)?

3. What is the mass of one molecule of HCl (hydrochloric acid)?

4.   What is the mass of one molecule of CO_2 (carbon dioxide)?

One conversion will let us change amu to the more familiar grams. This conversion also illustrates the importance of scientific notation in chemistry.

$$1.00 \text{ amu} = 1.67 \times 10^{-24} \text{ grams}$$

EXAMPLE 2   What is the mass of a hydrogen-peroxide molecule in grams? From Example 1, we know that the mass of hydrogen peroxide is 34.02 amu.

$$\frac{34.02 \text{ amu}}{1} \times \frac{1.67 \times 10^{-24} \text{ g}}{1.00 \text{ amu}} = 56.81 \times 10^{-24} \text{ g} = 5.68 \times 10^{-23} \text{ g}$$

5.   Change the masses you found for hydrochloric acid and for carbon dioxide to grams. (#3 and #4)

6.   Find the mass for $C_4H_{10}O$ (an anesthetic), and give your answer in grams.

Change from base 10 to the given base.

1. $80_{10} =$ _____ $_3$

2. $80_{10} =$ _____ $_5$

3. $80_{10} =$ _____ $_4$

4. $100_{10} =$ _____ $_6$

5. $1{,}352_{10} =$ _____ $_8$

6. $1{,}352_{10} =$ _____ $_6$

Change from the given base to base 10.

7. $563_7 =$ _____ $_{10}$

8. $441_5 =$ _____ $_{10}$

9. $2121_3 =$ _____ $_{10}$

10. $3421_5 =$ _____ $_{10}$

11. $6A8_{12} =$ _____ $_{10}$

12. $B81_{13} =$ _____ $_{10}$

Change from base 10 to the given base.

1. 95_{10} = _____ $_2$

2. 95_{10} = _____ $_5$

3. 95_{10} = _____ $_7$

4. 100_{10} = _____ $_8$

5. $1{,}352_{10}$ = _____ $_{12}$

6. $1{,}352_{10}$ = _____ $_9$

Change from the given base to base 10.

7. $11001_2 =$ _____ $_{10}$

8. $2121_7 =$ _____ $_{10}$

9. $465_7 =$ _____ $_{10}$

10. $3421_6 =$ _____ $_{10}$

11. $26A_{12} =$ _____ $_{10}$

12. $3B4_{20} =$ _____ $_{10}$

Change from base 10 to the given base.

1. 100_{10} = _____ 3

2. 245_{10} = _____ 6

Change from the given base to base 10.

3. 56_7 = _____ 10

4. 173_8 = _____ 10

Use scientific notation to solve. Give the answer to the nearest significant digit.

5. 300 x 7,000 x .8 =

6. 60 x .05 x 40,000 =

For #7–8, solve numerator and denominator first, then divide using scientific notation.

7. $\dfrac{9,000 \times .04}{3000,000 \times .2}$ = _____ =

8. $\dfrac{1.4 \times .005}{350,000}$ = _____ =

Solve.

9. $[(10^2)^{\frac{1}{2}}]^0$

10. $4^{\frac{3}{2}} \cdot 16^2 \cdot 64^{\frac{2}{3}} =$

11. $100^{\frac{3}{2}} \cdot (10^2)^4 =$

12. $D^{\frac{-1}{3}} \cdot D^6 \cdot D^{\frac{2}{3}} =$

13. 880 yards =_____ m

14. Your weight (pounds) =_____ kg

15. 1 gallon =_____ liters

16. Your weight (pounds) =_____ g

17. Look up how many square miles there are in India. Change the square miles to square feet.

18. If there are six billion people in the world, how many square feet would each person receive if everyone lived in India?

Find all possible factors.

19. $B^2 - A^2 =$

20. $C^4 - D^4 =$

Change from base 10 to the given base.

1. $100_{10} = $ _____ $_7$

2. $245_{10} = $ _____ $_8$

Change from the given base to base 10.

3. $2120_3 = $ _____ $_{10}$

4. $3210_4 = $ _____ $_{10}$

Use scientific notation to solve. Give the answer to the nearest significant digit.

5. $.032 \times 8,000 \times .7 = $

6. $.003 \times 500 = $

7. $12,400 \div .04 = $

8. $1,000,000 \div 5,000,000 = $

Solve.

9. $8^{\frac{4}{3}} = $

10. $(X^{\frac{4}{3}})^{\frac{1}{2}} = $

11. $A^{-5} A^4 A^{-3} A^{\frac{1}{2}} = $

12. $\dfrac{B^5 A^{-2}}{B^{-3} A^7} = $

13. 1 ton = _____ kg

14. 4 square feet = _____ square inches

15. Solve for E: $\dfrac{2.2}{11} = \dfrac{1.5}{E}$ (E ≠ 0)

16. Solve for B: $\dfrac{A}{B} = \dfrac{C}{D}$ (B and D ≠ 0)

17. Look up how many square miles there are in China.
Change the square miles to square feet.

18. If there are six billion people in the world, how many square feet would each person receive if everyone lived in China?

19. What fraction or decimal part of an acre is that? (Use 4.4×10^4 for the value of an acre.)

20. Graph 5Y + 4X ≥ 10.

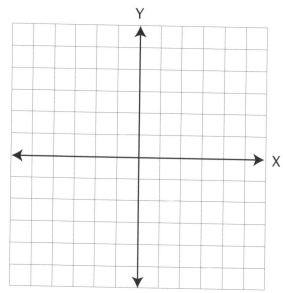

Change from base 10 to the given base.

1. 100_{10} = _____ $_9$

2. 245_{10} = _____ $_4$

Change from the given base to base 10.

3. $35AB_{12}$ = _____ $_{10}$

4. 404_5 = _____ $_{10}$

Use scientific notation to solve. Give the answer to the nearest significant digit.

5. $60,200,000 \times .507 =$

6. $2,000 \times 5,000 \times 400 =$

7. $90,000,000,000 \times .000021 =$

8. $40,000 \times 30,000 \div 60 =$

9. $(X^{\frac{2}{5}})(X^{\frac{1}{3}}) =$

10. $(X^{\frac{2}{5}})^{\frac{1}{3}} =$

11. $(X^{\frac{2}{3}})(X^{\frac{-1}{5}}) =$

12. $\dfrac{B^6 B C^{-4}}{C^9 C^{-4}} =$

13. 100 miles = _____ km   14. 14 cubic yards = _____ cubic feet

15. Solve for W: $\dfrac{.03}{2} = \dfrac{1.5}{W}$ (W ≠ 0)

16. Solve for A: 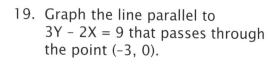 (Y and A ≠ 0)

17. Find all solutions of X and check: $3X^2 + 14X + 8 = 0$.

18. Change 3Y − 2X = 9 to slope-intercept form and graph the line.

19. Graph the line parallel to
    3Y − 2X = 9 that passes through
    the point (−3, 0).

20. Graph the line perpendicular to
    3Y − 2X = 9 that passes through
    the point (1, 0).

Computer programmers and computer engineers use base-16 math. This is referred to as hexadecimal math. We use the numbers 0–9 and the letters A–F to represent all 16 possibilities for hexadecimal base manipulation.

0	4	8	C
1	5	9	D
2	6	A	E
3	7	B	F

EXAMPLE 1 Convert 200 base 10 to its corresponding hexadecimal number.

$200 \div 16 = 12$ remainder 8. The answer is C8.

EXAMPLE 2 Convert 1BF base 16 to base 10.
$1(256) + 11(16) + 15(1) = 447$

Follow the directions.

1. Convert 225 base 10 to base 16.

2. Convert 888 base 10 to base 16.

3. Convert 500 base 16 to base 10.

4. Convert 750 base 16 to base 10.

Computer–graphics programs deal with three colors: red, green, and blue (R, G, B). Each of these colors is coded into a base–16 number and used in html (a language used on the Web). A six–digit number is used to tell the computer what color to display on the screen. The first two digits tell the amount of red, the next two are for green, and the final two are for blue. (Remember that you get different results from mixing light than you do from mixing pigment.)

EXAMPLE 3 #028003 would be a medium-green color with a little red and blue added. 02 is for red, 80 is for green, and 03 is for blue. (These numbers are in base 16, so they represent 02, 128, and 03 in base 10.)

5. What color will be displayed by the hexadecimal number 0101FF?

6. The number 000000 is defined as black. What number do you think is used to define white?

7. What color will be displayed by 00FFFF?

Answer the questions and graph each circle or ellipse.

Some problems on these two pages will have answers with radicals that cannot be simplified to whole numbers. Keep the radical in your answer and estimate to sketch your graph. For example:

$$\sqrt{2} \approx 1.4 \qquad \sqrt{3} \approx 1.7 \qquad \sqrt{5} \approx 2.2 \qquad \sqrt{6} \approx 2.4$$

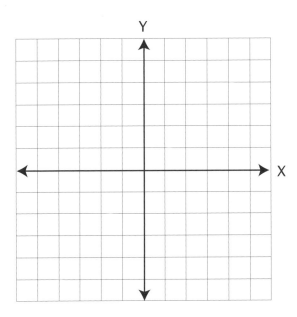

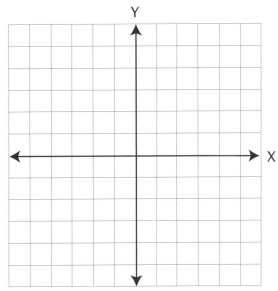

$$X^2 + Y^2 = 16 \qquad\qquad (X - 1)^2 + (Y - 2)^2 = 9$$

1. If X = 0, Y = _____ and _____ .

2. If Y = 0, X = _____ and _____ .

3. The center is _____ .

4. The radius is _____ .

5. If X = 1, Y = _____ and _____ .

6. If Y = 2, X = _____ and _____ .

7. The center is _____ .

8. The radius is _____ .

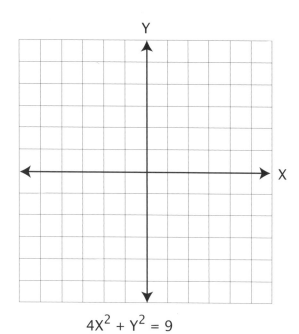

$$4X^2 + Y^2 = 9$$

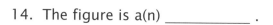

$$6X^2 + 4Y^2 = 12$$

9. If X = 0, Y = _____ and _____ .

10. If Y = 0, X = _____ and _____ .

11. The figure is a(n) _____ .

12. If X = 0, Y = _____ and _____ .

13. If Y = 0, X = _____ and _____ .

14. The figure is a(n) _____ .

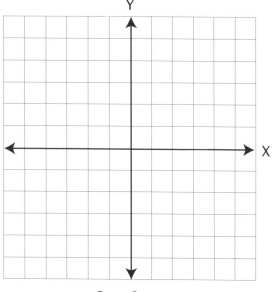

15. Graph: $X^2 + Y^2 = 25$.

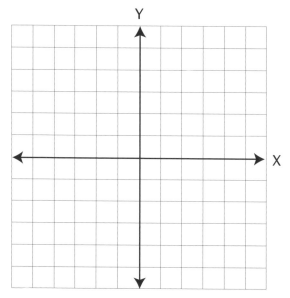

16. Graph: $(X + 3)^2 + (Y - 1)^2 = 4$.

Answer the questions and graph each circle or ellipse.

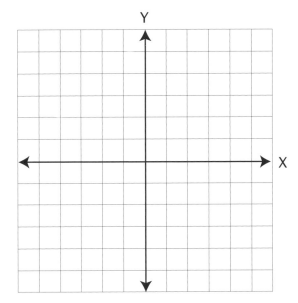

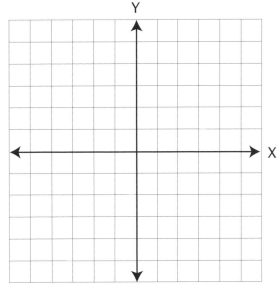

$$X^2 + Y^2 = 4$$

$$(X + 3)^2 + (Y - 4)^2 = 9$$

1. If X = 0, Y = _____ and _____ .

5. If X = –3, Y = _____ and _____ .

2. If Y = 0, X = _____ and _____ .

6. If Y = 4, X = _____ and _____ .

3. The center is _____ .

7. The center is _____ .

4. The radius is _____ .

8. The radius is _____ .

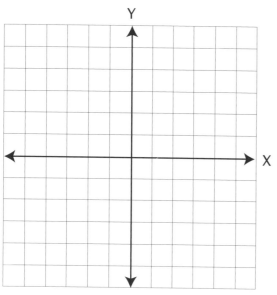

$$3X^2 + 2Y^2 = 12$$

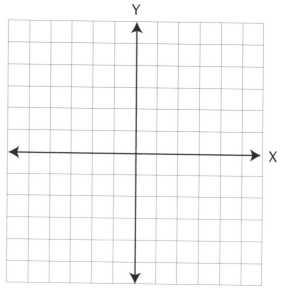

$$5X^2 + 3Y^2 = 15$$

9. If X = 0, Y = _____ and _____ .

12. If X = 0, Y = _____ and _____ .

10. If Y = 0, X = _____ and _____ .

13. If Y = 0, X = _____ and _____ .

11. The figure is a(n) _____ .

14. The figure is a(n) _____ .

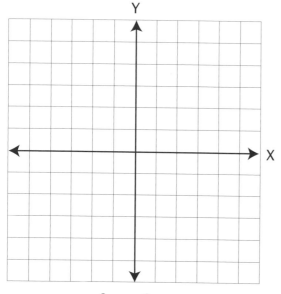

15. Graph: $X^2 + 5Y^2 = 20$

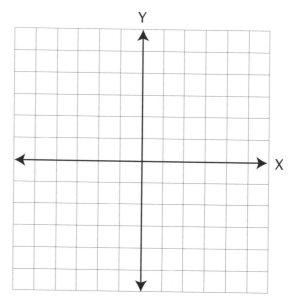

16. Graph: $(X + 4)^2 + (Y - 4)^2 = 16$

Answer the questions and graph each circle or ellipse.

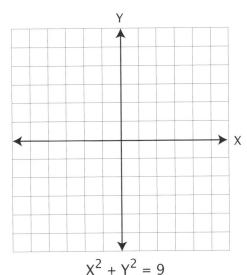

$X^2 + Y^2 = 9$

1. If X = 0, Y = _____ and _____ .

2. If Y = 0, X = _____ and _____ .

3. The center is _____ .

4. The radius is _____ .

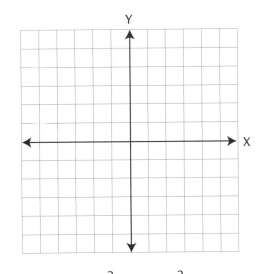

$(X - 1)^2 + (Y - 2)^2 = 9$

5. If X = 1, Y = _____ and _____ .

6. If Y = 2, X = _____ and _____ .

7. The center is _____ .

8. The radius is _____ .

$4X^2 + 9Y^2 = 36$

9. If X = 0, Y = _____ and _____ .

10. If Y = 0, X = _____ and _____ .

Change to a different base as indicated.

11. $1{,}721_{10} =$ _____ $_8$

12. $4{,}090_{10} =$ _____ $_5$

13. $654_7 =$ _____ $_{10}$

14. $8B0_{12} =$ _____ $_{10}$

Solve using scientific notation.

15. $1{,}000 \times 500 \times 70{,}000 =$

16. $.000058 \times .0023 =$

Solve by substitution.

17. $Y = 2X + 2$ and $Y + 4X = -4$

Solve by elimination, if possible.

18. $3Y - 2X = -1$ and $Y = 2/3 \, X + 1$

Find all possible factors.

19. $2Y^5 - 162Y =$

20. $Y^8 - 1 =$

Answer the questions and graph each circle or ellipse.

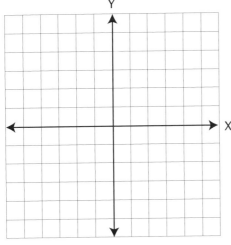

$2X^2 + 2Y^2 = 8$

1. If X = 0, Y = _____ and _____ .

2. If Y = 0, X = _____ and _____ .

3. The center is _____ .

4. The radius is _____ .

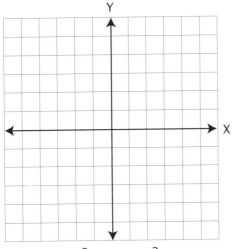

$(X + 1)^2 + (Y + 3)^2 = 4$

5. If X = –1, Y = _____ and _____ .

6. If Y = –3, X = _____ and _____ .

7. The center is _____ .

8. The radius is _____ .

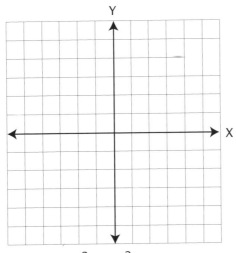

$9X^2 + 4Y^2 = 36$

9. If X = 0, Y = _____ and _____ .

10. If Y = 0, X = _____ and _____ .

Divide.

11. $X - 1\overline{)X^3 - 3X^2 + 3X - 1}$

12. $X - 2\overline{)8X^3 - 4X^2 + 5X + 1}$

Change to a different base as indicated.

13. $371_{10} =$ _____ $_4$

14. $215_{10} =$ _____ $_8$

15. $406_7 =$ _____ $_{10}$

16. $100_4 =$ _____ $_{10}$

Solve using scientific notation.

17. $(3 \times 10^{-5})(2 \times 10^{-2}) =$

18. $(4 \times 10^{-5})(5 \times 10^2) \div (2 \times 10^3) =$

Solve by substitution.

19. $Y = 3X - 1$ and $4Y = -3X - 19$

Solve for M.

20. $21 + 12M - 3M = 15M - 9$

Answer the questions and graph each circle or ellipse.

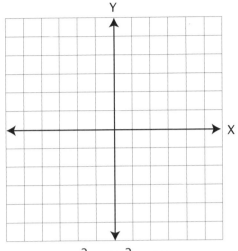

$3X^2 + 3Y^2 = 48$

1. If X = 0, Y = _____ and _____ .

2. If Y = 0, X = _____ and _____ .

3. The center is _____ .

4. The radius is _____ .

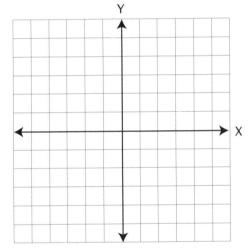

$3(X + 1)^2 + 3(Y + 3)^2 = 48$

5. If X = –1, Y = _____ and _____ .

6. If Y = –3, X = _____ and _____ .

7. The center is _____ .

8. The radius is _____ .

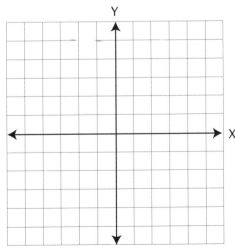

$9X^2 + 16Y^2 = 144$

9. If X = 0, Y = _____ and _____ .

10. If Y = 0, X = _____ and _____ .

Divide.

11. $X + 1 \overline{\smash{\big)}\ X^3 + 3X^2 + 3X + 1}$

12. $X + 2 \overline{\smash{\big)}\ X^3 + 4X^2 + 7X + 6}$

Solve as indicated.

13. $1,054_{10} =$ _____ $_6$

14. $101,111_2 =$ _____ $_{10}$

15. $50 \times 60 \bigcirc 55 \times 55$

16. 4 acres $\bigcirc$ 200,000 ft^2

17. $(4.2 \times 10^4) \div (6 \times 10^{-3}) =$

18. $[(7 \times 10^8)(8 \times 10^0)] \div [(4 \times 10^3)(1.4 \times 10^5)] =$

Find all possible factors.

19. $X^4 - 16 =$

Solve for A.

20. $1.25 + .8A - 1 = .3$

Johannes Kepler was a German astronomer who discovered that the planets move in an elliptical pattern around the sun. He developed three laws that are foundational to the study of astronomy.

Kepler's First Law: The orbits of the planets are ellipses, with the sun at one focus of the ellipse.

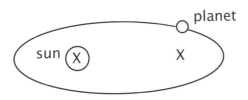

In *Geometry*, you will learn that if you measure from each focus to a point on the ellipse, and then add the two measurements, the sum is always the same. The foci on this ellipse are marked by "X."

Kepler's Second Law: Planets move faster when they are closer to the sun.

Kepler's Third Law: When the orbital time period and the orbital size of any planet are compared, the period is proportional to the 3/2 power of the orbit size. This may seem a little hard to understand, but it means that we can use the following formula to compare time of orbit (period) and length of orbit.

$$P^2 = A^3$$

P is the period of time required to go one time around the sun in earth years.

A is the length of the orbit in astronomical units (AU).

The astronomical unit is used by astronomers to make it easier to deal with very large numbers. The distance from the earth to the sun is 9.3×10^7 miles. This is recognized as one astronomical unit, or one AU. A planet that is twice as far from the sun as the earth is would be two AU from the sun. A planet that is one–half as far from the sun as the earth is would be .5 AU from the sun.

EXAMPLE   The orbit size of Venus is .615 AU. How many earth days does it take for Venus to revolve around the sun one time? Use a calculator to multiply and to find square roots. Remember what you know about significant digits when rounding your results.

$$P^2 = (.615)^3 \qquad\qquad P^2 = .233 \qquad\qquad P = .483$$

$365(.483) = 176 =$ the number of earth days for Venus to revolve around the sun

Follow the directions. Use significant digits when rounding your answers.

1.   Jupiter's orbit size is 11.8 AU. How many earth days does it take for Jupiter to make one revolution around the sun?

2.   A planet was discovered to have an orbit size of .241 AU. Is that planet Mercury or Pluto? (For this question, you may consider Pluto a planet!)

3.   The orbit size for Mars is 1.88 AU. How many earth days does it take for Mars to make one revolution around the sun?

4.   If a planet's year (time of one revolution) is 100 earth days, how many miles is this planet from the sun? In this case, P (the period or time of revolution) is known, and you must solve for A (distance in AU). You may need to consult the manual that came with your calculator to learn how to find a cube root. Don't forget to convert your answer from AU to miles.

Complete each table of values, then plot and draw each curve.
(You may plot more points if necessary.)

1. $Y = X^2$

X	Y
0	
1	
-1	
2	
-2	

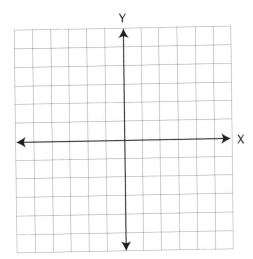

2. $XY = 6$

X	Y
2	
-2	
3	
-3	
1	
-1	
6	
-6	

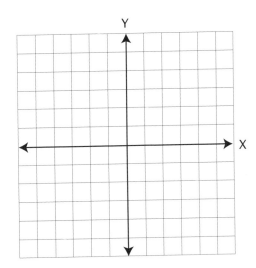

3. $Y = 2X^2$

X	Y
0	
1	
2	
3	
-1	
-2	

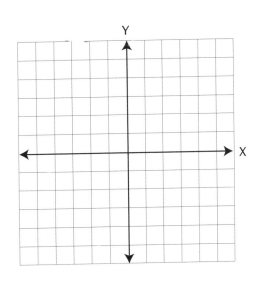

4.   XY = −2

X	Y
1	___
-1	___
2	___
-2	___
1/2	___
-1/2	___
4	___
-4	___

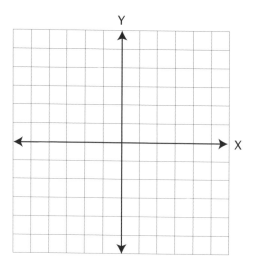

5.   Y = X^2 − 3

X	Y
0	___
1	___
-1	___
2	___
-2	___

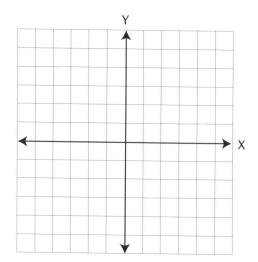

6.   XY = 8

X	Y
2	___
-2	___
4	___
-4	___
1 1/3	___
-1 1/3	___
6	___
-6	___

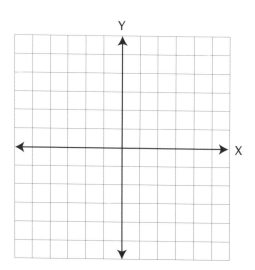

Complete each table of values, then plot and draw each curve.
(You may plot more points if necessary.)

1. $Y = 1/2 \, X^2$

X	Y
0	___
1	___
2	___
3	___
-1	___
-2	___

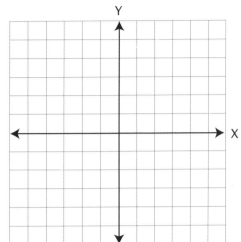

2. $XY = -3$

X	Y
-1	___
1	___
-3	___
3	___
1 1/2	___
-1 1/2	___
-2	___
2	___

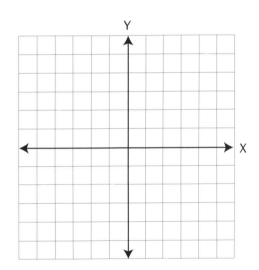

3. $Y = X^2 + 1$

X	Y
0	___
1	___
2	___
-1	___
-2	___

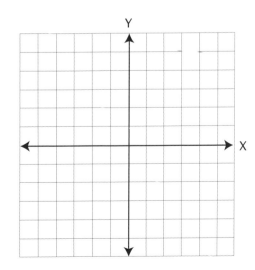

4. XY = –4

X	Y
1	
-1	
4	
-4	
1 1/3	
-1 1/3	
6	
-6	

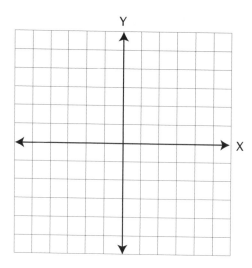

5. $Y = -X^2$

X	Y
0	
1	
2	
-1	
-2	

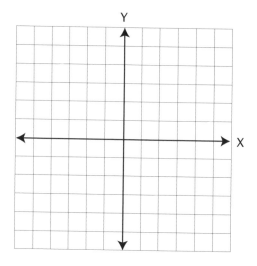

6. XY = 5

X	Y
1	
-1	
5	
-5	
1 1/4	
-1 1/4	
0	

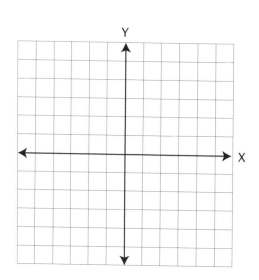

Complete each table of values, then plot and draw each curve.
(You may plot more points if necessary.)

1. $Y = X^2$

X	Y
0	____
1	____
-1	____
2	____
-2	____

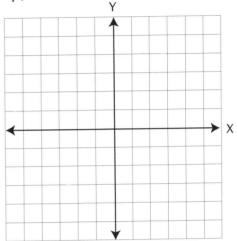

2. $XY = 1$

X	Y
1	____
-1	____
3	____
-3	____
5	____
-5	____

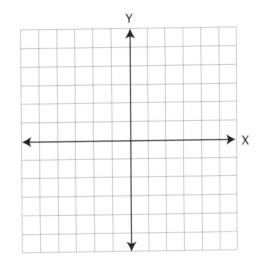

Tell what kind of graph each equation represents. Choose line, circle, ellipse, parabola, or hyperbola.

3. $Y = 4X + 5$

4. $X^2 + Y^2 = 16$

5. $2X^2 + 4Y^2 = 8$

6. $4X + 6Y - 4 = 0$

7. $XY = 4$

8. $Y = -X^2$

Solve as indicated.

9. $1{,}793_{12} = \underline{\hspace{2cm}}_{10}$

10. $131_{10} = \underline{\hspace{2cm}}_{5}$

11. $1{,}111_2 \bigcirc 202_3$

12. $2 \text{ ft}^2 \bigcirc 289 \text{ in}^2$

13. $(7 \times 10^{-8}) \div (1.4 \times 10^6) =$

14. $[(2.4 \times 10^{-4})(2.6 \times 10^5)] \div [(6 \times 10^{-5})(5.2 \times 10^{-7})] =$

15. $\dfrac{2}{3}X + \dfrac{4}{5} = -\dfrac{17}{30}$

16. $\dfrac{5}{6} - \dfrac{1}{3}X + \dfrac{4}{7} = 0$

17. $(78)(72) =$

18. Factor $Y^3 - Y$.

19. Graph a line that passes through $(-1, 1)$ and $(1, -4)$.

20. Find the equation of the line you graphed in #19.

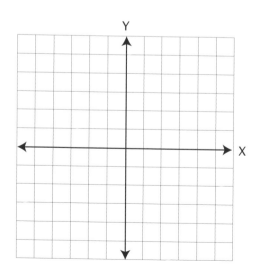

Complete each table of values, then plot and draw each curve.
(You may plot more points if necessary.)

1. $Y = 2X^2$

X	Y
0	
1	
-1	
2	
-2	

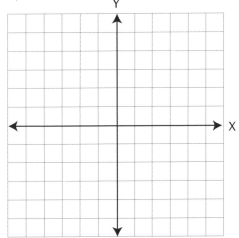

2. $XY = 6$

X	Y
.5	
-.5	
1	
-1	
2	
-2	
3	
-3	

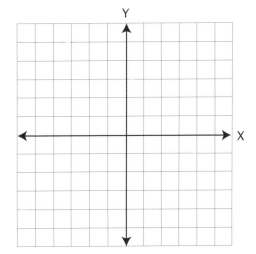

Tell what kind of graph each equation represents. Choose line, circle, ellipse, parabola, or hyperbola.

3. $Y = X^2 - 1$

4. $(X - 1)^2 + (Y - 3)^2 = 9$

5. $XY = 5$

6. $Y = 4X^2$

7. $X^2 + 3Y^2 = 12$

8. $Y = mX + B$

Solve as indicated.

9. $132_4 =$ _____ $_{10}$

10. $2{,}348_{10} =$ _____ $_8$

11. $|17 - 3| \cdot (-2)$ ◯ $-5^2 - 4$

12. $47 \cdot 43$ ◯ 45^2

13. $(6 \times 10^7)(2.5 \times 10^{-9}) =$

14. $[(1.1 \times 10^{-9})(1.5 \times 10^8)] \div [(5 \times 10^1)(3 \times 10^{-6})] =$

15. $Y^{-2} \div Y^{-6} =$

16. $.25$ miles = _____ feet

Simplify and add if possible.

17. $\dfrac{C^6 D^3 C^2}{D^{-9} D^{-2} C^8}$

18. $3X^{-2} Y^2 + \dfrac{4Y^4 Y^0 Y^{-2}}{X^{-1}} =$

19. Graph the line represented by
    $Y = -4X + 5$.

20. Graph the line that is perpendicular
    to the line in #20 passing through
    the point (1, 1).

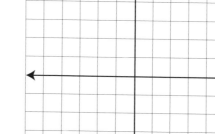

Complete each table of values, then plot and draw each curve.
(You may plot more points if necessary.)

1. $Y = 3X^2$

X	Y
0	___
1	___
-1	___
2	___
-2	___

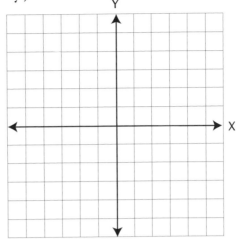

2. $XY = -10$

X	Y
1	___
-1	___
2	___
-2	___
5	___
-5	___

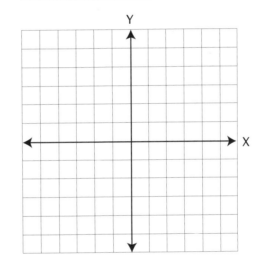

Tell what kind of graph each equation represents. Choose line, circle, ellipse, parabola, or hyperbola.

3. $2X^2 + 3Y^2 = 36$

4. $XY = 15$

5. $Y = 4X + 13$

6. $(X - 3)^2 + (Y + 4)^2 = 18$

7. $8Y + 2X + 6 = 0$

8. $4X^2 + 4Y^2 = 12$

Solve as indicated.

9. $151_7 = $ _____ $_{10}$

10. $291_{10} = $ _____ $_4$

11. $|3 \cdot 2 \cdot (-2)| \bigcirc 24 \div (-3)$

12. $(3^2)^{\frac{1}{3}} \bigcirc (287)^2$

13. Express with scientific notation: ninety-three million.

14. Express with scientific notation: thirty-eight thousandths.

15. 900 grams = _____ ounces

16. $1 \text{ yd}^2 = $ _____ in^2

17. Factor $A^3 - 25A$.

18. Factor $243 - 3X^4$.

19. Debbie was picking flowers. She had X flowers in her hand. Rachel gave her X + 4 flowers. Debbie picked 5 more flowers, then she dropped one and gave 2X flowers to her mom. If Debbie now has twice as many in her hand as she started with, how many did she start with? (Write an equation and solve for X.)

20. The teacher gave five points for every algebra problem the students did correctly. Roger got D correct and Tyler got 4 correct. Together they earned 45 points. How many problems did Roger do correctly?

Parabolas occur in many places in everyday life. One example is a suspension bridge, and another is the path of a projectile, such a cannon ball or an arrow shot into the air.

When graphed, a parabola with a right-side-up "U" shape has a lowest point or vertex. This is the point that has the smallest value for Y. It is called the minimum or minima. A parabola with an upside-down "U" shape has a highest point, also called the vertex. This is the point that has the largest value for Y. It is called the maximum or maxima.

Parabola-application problems are often solved by finding the vertex. The point (h, k) is used to designate the x and y coordinates of the vertex.

Do not worry if you find this challenging. It will be taught again in *Algebra 2*.

EXAMPLE

Suppose you have 400 feet of fencing with which to enclose your field. What dimensions will give the maximum fenced area?

If L is the length and W is the width of the fenced area, then 2L + 2W = 400, and L = 200 – W.

Area = Length x Width = (200 – W)(W) = $-W^2$ + 200W

restated: k = $-h^2$ + 200h

This parabola has a negative coefficient for the squared term, so it has an up-side-down shape.

Therefore, the vertex is the highest point or maximum. Solving for the vertex will give you the width that yields the maximum area. Use the formula below to find "h."

$h = -\dfrac{b}{2a}$ Where a is the coefficient of the squared term and b is the coefficient of the second term.

$h = -\dfrac{200}{2(-1)} = 100$ Substitute values from the original equation above, and solve for h.

$k = -(100)^2 + (200)(100) = 10,000$ Substitute the value of h into the original
equation, and solve for k.

k = maximum area = 10,000 ft^2 and h = width = 100 ft.

If the width is 100 ft, the length must also be 100 ft because 100 x 100 = 10,000. Thus the most efficient rectangular shape is a square.

Follow the directions.

1. John has 1,200 feet of fencing material. He wants to fence a corral in two sections as shown in the drawing. What are the dimensions of the largest fenced area for his corral? Hint: Start with 2L + 3W = 1,200.

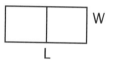

2. John decides to build the same structure as in #1, using an existing fence for one side. What are the dimensions of the largest area that he can enclose with the same amount of fencing as in #1?

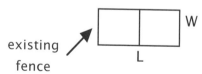

Symbols & Tables

IMPERIAL WEIGHTS & MEASURES

2 cups = 1 pint (pt)
2 pints = 1 quart (qt)
4 quarts = 1 gallon (gal)
8 pints = 1 gallon
12 inches (in) = 1 foot (ft)
3 feet = 1 yard (yd)
5,280 feet = 1 mile (mi)
16 ounces (oz) = 1 pound (lb)
1 ton = 2,000 pounds

1 acre of land = 43,560 ft^2
1 cord of wood = 4' x 4' x 8' = 128 ft^3
1 yard of carpet = 3' x 3' = 1 yd^2
1 yard of concrete = 3' x 3' x 3' = 1 yd^3

IMPERIAL TO METRIC

1 inch ≈ 2.5 centimeters (cm)
1 yard ≈ .9 meters (m)
1 mile ≈ 1.6 kilometers (km)
1 ounce ≈ 28 grams (g)
1 pound ≈ .45 kilograms (kg)
1 quart ≈ .95 liters (l or L)

METRIC TO IMPERIAL

1 centimeter ≈ .4 inches
1 meter ≈ 1.1 yards
1 kilometer ≈ .62 miles
1 gram ≈ .035 ounces
1 kilogram ≈ 2.2 pounds
1 liter ≈ 1.06 quarts

SYMBOLS

<	less than
>	greater than
≤	less than or equal to
≥	greater than or equal to
=	equal in numerical value
≠	not equal
≈	approximately equal
$\sqrt{}$	square root (radical sign)
%	percent
⊥	perpendicular
∥	parallel
1'	1 foot
1"	1 inch
| X | = X	absolute value of X equals X
|-X | = X	absolute value of negative X equals X

FORMULAS

Standard Form of Equations

line	$AX + BY = C$
circle	$AX^2 + AY^2 = C$
ellipse	$AX^2 + BY^2 = C$
parabola	$Y = X^2$
hyperbola	$XY = C$

**Slope-Intercept Form
of the Equation of a Line**

$$Y = mX + b$$

where m = slope
b = Y-intercept

$$\text{Slope of a line} = \frac{up}{over} = \frac{rise}{run} = \frac{Y_2 - Y_1}{X_2 - X_1}$$

PROPERTIES

Associative Property

$$(A + B) + C = A + (B + C)$$

$$(A \times B) \times C = A \times (B \times C)$$

Commutative Property

$$A + B = B + A$$

$$A \times B = B \times A$$

Distributive Property

$$A(B + C) = AB + AC$$

MISCELLANEOUS

Exponents

$$X^a \cdot X^b = X^{a+b}$$

$$X^a \div X^b = X^{a-b}$$

$$X^{-a} = \frac{1}{X^a}$$

$$\left(X^a\right)^b = X^{ab}$$

$$X^{\frac{1}{a}} = \sqrt[a]{X}$$

Order of Operations

<u>Pa</u>rachute <u>Ex</u>pert <u>My</u> <u>D</u>ear <u>Au</u>nt <u>Sa</u>lly

1) parentheses
2) exponents
3) multiplication and division
4) addition and subtraction

Rules for Divisibility

Number is divisible by

2	if it ends in even number
3	if digits add to multiple of 3
9	if digits add to multiple of 9
5	if it ends in 5 or 0

METRIC MEASURES

1,000 millimeters (mm) - 1 meter (m)
100 centimeters (cm) - 1 meter
10 decimeters (dm) - 1 meter
10 meters = 1 dekameter (dkm or dam)
100 meters = 1 hectometer (hm)
1,000 meters = 1 kilometer (km)

1,000 milligrams (mg) - 1 gram (g)
100 centigrams (cg) - 1 gram
10 decigrams (dg) - 1 gram
10 grams = 1 dekagram (dkg or dag)
100 grams = 1 hectogram (hg)
1,000 grams = 1 kilogram (kg)

1,000 milliliters (ml) - 1 liter (l or L)
100 centiliters (cl) - 1 liter
10 deciliters (dl) - 1 liter
10 liters = 1 dekaliter (dkl or dal)
100 liters = 1 hectoliter (hl)
1,000 liters = 1 kiloliter (kl)

Glossary

A

Absolute value - lines used to show that the value of an expression is positive

Additive inverse - a number that can be added to another to make zero

Algebra - system that uses letters to represent unknown numbers and variables; base X

Analytic geometry - algebra shown "geometrically" on a graph

Area - the number of square units in a rectangle or other two-dimensional figure

Associative property - the way terms are grouped does not affect the answer; true for addition and multiplication

Astronomical unit (AU) - the distance from the earth to the sun (93,000,000 miles)

Atomic mass unit (amu) - a very small unit used to measure the weight, or mass, of molecules

B

Base - the number on which a place value system is built; our decimal system is base 10

Binomial - an algebraic expression with two terms

Break–even point

Break–even point - in a business, the point where revenue and costs are the same

C

Cartesian coordinate system - the X and Y graphing system named for René Descartes

Circle - the geometric figure formed by cutting a cone with a plane parallel to its base

Coefficient - the number that is multiplied by the variable

Commutative property - the order of terms does not affect the answer; true for addition and multiplication

Composite numbers - may be factored in more than one way; not prime

Cone - a three-dimensional figure rising to a point from a circular base, as in an ice cream cone

Cost - all the expenses of doing business; includes fixed costs and the cost of labor and materials

Counting numbers - the numbers used to count items

Cube root - the number that when multiplied by itself three times, produces the given number

437

D - E

Distributive property - a common factor is "distributed" among the terms of an equation

Elimination - method of solving a simultaneous equations by subtracting

Ellipse - a "stretched" circle with two centers, or foci

Exponent - tells how many times a number is multiplied by itself

Exponential increase or growth - result of repeatedly raising an amount by a given exponent

F - G

Factor - a number that may be multiplied by another to give the desired product

Factors - the numbers being multiplied to find a product

Factoring - finding the factors of a given number

Greatest common factor (GCF) - the largest number that will divide evenly into two or more numbers

H - L

Hexadecimal math - uses base-16 number system

Hyperbola - two congruent open curves that face in opposite directions on a graph

Integers - the positive and negative counting numbers and zero

Irrational numbers - cannot be written as fractions; in decimal form are non-repeating and non-terminating

Latitude - horizontal lines that measure the north-south distance from the equator

Least common multiple (LCM) - the smallest number that is a multiple of two or more other numbers

Line - an infinite number of connected points

M - O

Magnitude - size or force

Multiplicative inverse - a reciprocal; a number that when multiplied by another has a product of one

Natural numbers - another name for counting numbers

Origin - the point where the X- and Y-axes intersect on a graph, or the starting point of a ray

P - Q

Parabola - a single open curve on a graph, defined by $Y = X^2$

Parallel lines - two straight lines in the same plane that do not intersect

Perpendicular lines - two lines that form right angles when they intersect

Perimeter - the distance around the outside of a two-dimensional figure

Pitch - used by carpenters to describe the steepness of a roof

Postulate - assumed to be true, but cannot be proven

Polynomial - an algebraic expression with more than one term

Profit - in a business, the difference between revenue and all the costs of doing business

Pythagorean theorem - describes the relationship between the legs and the hypotenuse of a right triangle $(L^2 + L^2 = H^2)$

Quadrant - one of the four sections formed by the axes of a Cartesian graph

R

Radical - a numeral written with a square root sign

Rational number - the result of dividing two whole numbers; can be a whole number, decimal or fraction, any number that can be written as a ratio or fraction; including a fraction in the decimal form

Real numbers - includes all rational and irrational numbers

Reciprocal - the fraction that when multiplied by another fraction equals one; if N/D, then reciprocal is D/N

Resultant vector - the combination or addition of two vectors

Revenue - the total amount of money resulting from the sale of merchandise or services

S

Scatter diagram - a graph where the plotted points do not form a recognizable pattern

Scientific notation - uses exponents to write large and small numbers in order to make them easier to use

Significant digits - the number of places in a number that reflect the accuracy of a measurement

Simultaneous equations - two equations for which a common solution is sought

Slope - on a graph, the "rise" of a line over its "run;" tells how steep a line is

Square roots - the factors of a square

Substitution - a method of solving simultaneous equations by expressing one unknown in terms of the other

T - Z

Trinomial - an algebraic expression with three terms

Unit multiplier - an expression equal to one; used to convert measures

Vector - a unit of measure that includes direction and magnitude

Velocity - the speed of an object

Vertex - the highest or lowest point of a parabola

Volume - the number of cubic units that can be contained in a three-dimensional shape

Whole numbers - the counting numbers and zero

X-axis - horizontal axis of a Cartesian graph

Y-axis - vertical axis of a Cartesian graph

Y-intercept - the point where a line crosses the Y-axis